HAVE JUMP SHOT WILL TRAVEL

HAVE JUMP SHOT WILL TRAVEL

WILL TRAVEL

A NOVEL BY

Charles Rosen

ARBOR HOUSE
New York

Library of Congress Catalog Card Number:74–18158

ISBN: 0–87795–106–3

Manufactured in the United States of America

To Susan

NATIONAL
ANTHEM

Now there's a certain thing that
I love from my friend, Moss,
That fellow who never blushes.
And that is that one must always
Flush out his house,
If he don't expect to be housing flushes.

Open the door, Richard,
I've heard it said before.
Open the door, Richard,
I've heard it said before.
But I ain't gonna hesitate no more.

"Better take care of all of your
Memories," said Nick,
"For you cannot relive them.
And remember when you're out there,
Trying to heal the sick,
That you must always first forgive them."

Open the door, Richard,
I've heard it said before.
Open the door, Richard,
I've heard it said before.
But I ain't gonna hesitate no more.

—BOB DYLAN

FIRST QUARTER

CHAPTER ONE

FOUR MONTHS AGO, President–General Manager Arnold Pechman called to inform me that I had been drafted by the Wellington Rifles of the Atlantic Professional Basketball Association. I was seriously considering getting an agent until I discovered that any large, ambulatory white body who lived within 150 miles of any team in the league, who had not been drafted by either the NBA or the ABA and who had averaged over 10 points a game in his senior year in college was certain to be plucked by the APBA. About two-thirds of those so chosen simply break into hysterical laughter, hang up the phone and go on about their lives. The rest of us—after surviving a weekend of tryouts to which we are asked to "bring a friend"—become mindless basketball vegetables. I'm kind of a gigantic, but friendly, clove of garlic.

The league itself is made up of six tiny coal towns in Pennsylvania and two hamlets in New Jersey—but that's this year. The owners sniff around for a better deal immediately after the ink has dried on both sets of books at the conclusion of any given season. A "better deal," by the way, translates as free use of the local junior-high-school gym on Saturday or Sunday evenings and reduced advertising rates in the local gazette.

As far as the players are concerned, the APBA is to professional basketball as the Brooklyn Home for the Aged is to a hospital. All of them are incurably lame—some have diseased jump shots, some need hand transplants and those in the wards are over the hill and halfway into the next valley. One or two are on the way up. Several APBA players have made it into the bigs—people like Bob Love, Mike Riordan, Ray Scott and Harthorne Wingo of the Knicks. About the same percentage that recovers from terminal cancer.

As for me . . . well, I tell myself that it's just a way of keeping my heart beating and of earning some extra bucks. And, besides, I always did like salads. But every time I break into my two-point shuffle, I search the stands for the likes of Red Holzman. Fortunately, I don't score too often, so my fantasies are kept well under control.

What else? . . . My name is Robert Stephen Lassner, but you can call me "Bo"—I'm 6 foot 8, 225 pounds and I averaged 20 points a game for Hunter College in New York City. I'm not inclined to work hard enough to get into real good shape so I fake a limp whenever I have to run hard. My real problem, however, is that I'm too much of a spectator to play effectively—whenever someone lays a nice feed on me, I say "Good pass" while I'm shooting the lay-up. There's too much useless information fermenting inside my head for me to concentrate on anything, let alone basketball. But what I can do is shoot like a little man. The fracture is that I also rebound and play defense like a little man . . . about Tom Thumb little. Let's put it this way, the only shot I ever blocked during my career at Hunter was one of my own. I think I was waving to some chick with one hand while I was shooting with the other.

Anyway, I made the Rifles' squad primarily because I was the only white player who showed up. Pechman tried to remedy the situation once the season began by signing a beer belly named Clarence Fitzgerald from a bar league in Wellington to a $25-a-game contract. Clarence plays even less than I do but he comes from a large litter and at two dollars a pop they all attend every one of our home games. So Pechman added another pair of blue eyes and made some extra change at the same time.

I'm sure a blue-haired canasta queen somewhere in St. Petersburg is *qvelling* like crazy from her Arnold.

Arnold's warriors finished first in the division, mainly because the YMCA where the Pittsfield Blues play was condemned during the last week of the season and we got to play an extra home game against them. We were 21 and 0 at home and wound up with a record of 25 and 15, one game ahead of the Blues. For the past three weeks we've been busy beating Pittsfield 3 games to 2 in our quest for the traditional Golden Pick (a treasured bauble which the owner of the APBA's championship team gets to display in his living room for a year). And like my teammate Foothead Jones says, "That's the onliest pick I ever saw in my ten years in this here lig!"

All of this hee-haw is the reason why I was standing like a fool in the rain on the corner of Canal Street and the Bowery waiting for Lacey Freeman to pick me up for the drive down to Wellington. We were only seven hours away from the start of the championship playoffs with the Elizabeth Miners . . . and it was pouring . . . and that fucken bastard was a half hour late. I couldn't even duck into a doorway because he wouldn't even consider slowing down if he didn't see me standing right here on the spot. And there's nothing like being absolutely wet to remind me just how big, clumsy and vulnerable my body really is. The rain slapped at me and coated my face with a damp, gray jelly, and I could see exactly how indefensible my perimeters were.

So I just stood there for 30 minutes feeling like Frankenstein taking his last dip in the lagoon—and after a little while longer, Lacey wheeled his Cadillac up to the curb. The bas-

15

tard actually kept me waiting in the rain while he fiddled with the automatic door lock.

When it finally opened, I lurched inside, steaming and dripping as much as possible all over his back seat. I tried to ignore his switchblade stare but he refused to move the car until I took a towel out of my bag and started drying myself.

"Where the fuck were you?" I said, much more seriously than I had intended.

I could see his modest afro sticking out from beneath his wide-brimmed suede hat as he drove through the light Sunday traffic. I'll guarantee you that a couple of years ago, Lacey's hair was baked, fried and laid to the side. Whatever else I can say about him, Lacey does a very convincing impersonation of a nigger.

"I was where it was warm and dry," he laughed. "You could always take the bus if you ain't happy with the service . . . and leave the drivin' to them."

Lacey actually intimidated me into trying that once, but I pissed all over my pants trying to wedge myself into a functional position in the tiny bathroom, and I had to stay in there waiting for it to dry. And by the time I got back to my seat the chick I had met in the terminal was off with someone else. So Lacey's was the only song I knew the words to, and while I was singing I always felt impelled to do a blackface.

"No thanks, Lace," I said. "Greyhounds got no soul."

Just like a fucken line from "Plastic Fly," but Foothead snorted politely from the front seat and handed me a half-spent joint. I really didn't feel much like turning on with either of them, but I bowed to the demands of diddie-bop diplomacy. Maybe it would be easier to recall my ambassador.

Foothead at least is capable of an occasional abstract thought—in fact he may have been around when the first one was invented. He's also the Grand Old Fart of the league, but nobody knows just how old he really is, or where he was born. Foot claims to be "from" Los Angeles, but Lacey is always quick to remind him, "Ain't no nigger ever *from* L.A. They just wind up there."

Foothead's real name is Constantine, but his skull leans so far out that the sun never shines on the back of his neck. If I could ever teach him to sing, get him to wear shoelaces on his nose and stand on his head, we could make a fortune selling him as "The Pedal Extremity."

Foot's down-home edicts on the quality of a ballplayer, a chick, a meal or a ballgame are usually definitive. If Foot says, "We let this motherfucker go home," then we know the game has been *lost* and the scramble for points can officially begin. During tryouts somebody brought a Bed-Stuy school-yard Captain Marvel along with him. Foot inspected his game for a few minutes and then put the Word on him: "His shit ain' worth shit." And the Big Red Cheese took the next bus home.

Despite his hound-dogisms, there's something almost supernatural about Foothead—he definitely has a tap somewhere along the Divine Placenta. Even though he's always in the middle of the shotgun fire of jive platitudes, Foot never gets hit—and when he lets one fly he never misses. One of my many constant fears was that someday soon I'd be seeing Foot's diamond-black eyes peering at me through the sight of his rusty old squirrel gun. Needless to say, I treated him with the utmost respect and I never ate nuts in his presence.

But the one reason why everybody else digs the man is much more mercenary—he can't shoot to save his wrinkled old ass. And if he can't dunk the ball he won't even bother throwing it up at all. Naturally, this means more points and more money for everybody on the club. But Foot is a center

17

and so am I—so the only time I get to play is when he's in foul trouble. Of course, this only happens on the road.

I really thought I had the whole thing packaged nicely: Foot is a pronouncer, Lacey is a cheap-shot wise ass and I was too wet to talk, so we maintained radio silence as we drove through the Holland Tunnel . . . although Foot did light up and spread some smoke around again. I was managing a nice buzz in spite of myself, but when we reached the toll booths, Lacey glared at me in the rear-view mirror and said one word: "Dig!"

Nothing brings Lacey a more wicked rush than spoiling a nice high, but remembering the Piss on Your Pants Polka I obediently handed him five wet dollar bills for my share of gas, tolls and wear-and-tear on his back seat. His eyeballs ka-chunged and rang up at least $3 profit.

I've never heard anybody without a cunt say anything nice about Brother Lacey. He's about 6–4, 210 pounds and his skin is hard-brown and pebbled like a dog's first shit of the day. And money is the bone he chews on. He claims that the $150 a game that Pechman slips him doesn't even keep his shoes shined. Lacey is a super-frog looking for a small-enough pond—and the APBA is just a little too big around the balls to suit him.

Nobody is sure what Lacey's during-the-week gig is, but it certainly causes him enough worrying. At our home games in Wellington, whenever one of the Rifles scores, a recorded "shot" is fired over the loudspeaker. And whenever he has spotted a couple of unidentified black Cadillacs parked outside the gym, the sound makes Lacey hit the floor and scramble for the nearest exit.

But the man can shoot—and as far as I'm concerned that

covers a limbo full of sins. The community of great shooters (like morons and the physically deformed) know that we have all been personally bumped by the Greatest Shooter of All. So the edge is usually off Lacey's nastiness when he gets nasty with me.

Ten minutes out of the tunnel we were in Journal Square, Jersey City, waiting for one Wilfred W. Williams. I once asked Will how come most niggers have two first names, or last names like White, Brown, Black and Gray. He said it was because their ancestors were all slaves at one time. I mean, shit, "Lassner" is probably Russian for "Here come the Cossacks!" But I remembered to act humble and appropriately guilty at the time.

Will averages 43 points a game for the Rifles—he's the fifth leading scorer in the league—so Lacey waited quietly during the five minutes it took for him to get there. I'm sure he was creaming to split, but Foot would never had stood for it.

When he finally materialized, Will jumped into the back seat with me. "Hey, paleass. How you doin'?"

I half-closed my eyes to let him know I was stoned and not interested in his patter—and I handed him the still-smoking remains of Foot's last joint.

"On time," Will said as he toked it all in. "How's the dope business this week, Lace? String out any nine-year-olds?"

Lacey grinned broadly. "Can You Top This" ghetto style was about to begin. "Ask me no questions and I'll tell you no lies."

"Satan, get your ass behind me," Will said, with an exaggerated Southern drawl. "There ain't nothin' like a religious nigger . . . ain't they, Bo?"

Every so often, Will would come on with something like

19

that which untied a few of the packages. But, for the moment, I merely nodded wisely as Will laughed and gave five to the back of Foot's head.

"Hey, Pappa Foot, we gonna beat those suckers tonight?"

"No doubt about tonight," said Foot, "but next time jus' might be diff'ent."

And Foothead doesn't even lie when he's sleeping. There aren't any playoff shares or any stuff like that in the APBA. All through playoffs we still get paid by the game, and you can go to the bank on every single playoff round in the league's history going to a full five games. Our boxscores should be printed in "Variety."

After some more carbonated dialogue, Foot and Will fell out leaving instructions with me that they be kissed awake when we hit Goldy's Diner, 20 miles out of Wellington. While Will was asleep, Lacey felt the need to stick him one after the buzzer.

"Hey, Bo," he whispered, "poke that motherfucker, he's snoring like an old lady."

When I first hooked into the Lacey Shuttle, I really didn't know what to make of all the snappy talk. I watched and listened for a while—and eventually I felt secure enough to venture an occasional one-liner. I was even permitted to call Will an "uppity nigger" one time when we were all stoned. But I could never feel comfortable with them—I memorized some key words but they never came out right. Two weeks of this and I became paranoidly convinced that they were all involved in a conspiracy to pull on my chain. I was positive that my every word was repeated at parties all over Harlem and Brownsville. I mean they were friendly, but they made it clear that I was nothing but a white trampoline. Foot, of course, was the exception.

When I first realized that Will and Lacey didn't "like" me, I was a little wounded. I tried to protect myself after that by keeping my cynical distance, but once in a great while I would catch a bit of comfort in Will's eyes and I would jump for that magic metaphor that would force us both to acknowledge each other as poor fellow creatures who were identically cursed by the inevitability of both life and death. But I always seemed to roll snake-eyes and the door would shut again.

The one thing I never did try was to sheath my bent foil and let them see for themselves who I really was. The trouble, however, was that when I was with Lacey and Will I never quite knew who I really was. In their company I always felt like a second-string center who was getting paid for being white. And it was easier to fulfill their expectations than it was to attempt to deal with my own program. Anyway . . . in my universe, I always had the last, and the most potent, word.

It was awkward, but teaching Fizz Ed to a bunch of off-the-wall kids is even worse. With the tax-free, off-the-books, 150 bucks I collect on a usual weekend I only have to substitute in Herman Ryder Junior High School once a week during the season. But after tonight's game there would only be four more checks, so I had more reasons than I really needed to be nervous and irritable.

Goldy's was an important pit stop, especially for those ballplayers who had nothing definite working for them after the game. It wasn't Gallagher's, but it did function as insurance to make sure that we didn't commit the venal sin of

21

getting into the Wellingtonian wasteland too early. So all the wretched odds and ends from both teams would agglutinate there every Sunday night to shoot the shit, pick up on the grope-ies who also swarmed there, possibly get a quick Roto-Rooter blow job in the bathroom—do anything to pass the time except eat the food.

We were on our second cup of swill when three of the Miners came bopping in. One of them was Artie Brennan, one of the few white guards in the league and a notorious baby fucker. "Ain' nothing like a tight pussy," was his rationale . . . but Foot had Spoken: "The poor fella's probably jus' got a half a dick." Cody Wells .was there also—a young veteran from Newark whose brittle physique was the only thing keeping him from a long career as the tenth man on an ABA second-division team.

But the most notable presence was Tarzan Cooper, a Br'er Bear with a huge right arm instead of a club and a hibernating brain to match. TC had played with the Globies years ago but he was now precariously balanced on the edge of 36 and the spokes had fallen out of his wheels. If he caught you though, he could still roll over you bad. He's 6 foot 9 and a heaplike 270 pounds. Foothead swears that TC has callouses on his knuckles from using them as brakes.

The three of them filled the booth adjoining ours. Brennan's head was rotating like the red light on a police car as he tried to pick out a nubile teeny-fucker for his evening's violations. Cooper was industriously bending his spoon into a knot, but it was Cody who spoke first.

"You got any partying laid out for tonight?"

Lacey and Will were sadly shaking their heads, when TC suddenly bellowed and threw his silverware to the floor.

"Quick, Lacey," I whispered much too loudly. "Throw him a banana." But it was the wrong time to buy a seat at the gaming table.

"You muthafucka," Tarzan aimed a murderous paw in my direction. "All you muthafuckas . . . ain' none of you gonna be in no shape for no partyin' after we kick your ass tonight!"

Lacey broke into one of his especially sly grins. "What's the hap, TC? You caught Cheetah fucken 'round with your lady Jane?"

"You laugh now," Tarzan stammered, "but I'll be lookin' for you."

I could read his hairy face as easily as Goldy's menu—and both were enough to make me sick. TC was really counting down. We had played the Miners four times during the season and while Cooper had executed his bully's game with intensity, I had never seen his face rippling with the mad urge to destroy before. He was uncontrollably infuriated by Lacey's meager insult and he was on the verge of pounding on his tormentor's head right here and now.

I'm very much in favor of a little mayhem being performed on any part of Lacey's body—especially in lieu of mine—and I therefore felt a twinge of a missed merry-go-round ride when TC merely growled a curse and retreated to a solitary table in the corner.

"Why's his ass up?" Will asked.

Cody informed us that Irving Rudson, the Miners' owner, called every one of his ballplayers last night and promised them a bonus of $25 if they beat us tonight. It also seems that Tarzan, who had played the funny game for so many years, had simultaneously decided that this was his last chance to show the world that he really was a quality ballplayer. He

23

wanted to retire from the arena and take a couple of bleeding Christians with him.

True as that probably was, I somehow got the feeling that TC's blitzkrieg had much more sinister overtones.

Mix all of this together, heat to the point of boiling and you get one Foothead Popover nicely encased in an eyebrow-to-toenail cast. It's a good thing we were playing at home that night.

TIME OUT

CHAPTER Two

THE RIFLES' DRESSING ROOM was situated directly below the scoreboard. During the week it functioned as office, shower and bathroom for Wellington Junior High's two physical-education teachers. An initial-carved wooden desk with broken drawer locks, and an antique spring-balance scale had been pushed over against the far wall. The only concessions made to our comfort were a stack of maimed folding chairs and ten large nails which had been hammered at eye level into another wall. There were also several charts and signs clinging desperately to the faded gray wall over the desk—several strips of yellowed Scotch tape marked the fall from grace of last year's bell schedule and class rosters. Most of the surviving signs were hand-lettered reminders to the Wellington Junior High School football team that the only thing standing between them and creeping faggotry was the blind-siding of other 13-year-olds—"It's not the size of the man in the fight, it's the size of the fight in the man," and that old evergreen, "When the going gets tough, the tough get going." It must be nice to live in a parallel world. But my personal favorite was a diet wheel which informed the likes of Lacey and Foothead exactly how many green leafy vegetables they should be eating every day.

Needless to say, the place was teeming with bodies—unless you were taking a shower or a shit some part of you was bothering some part of somebody else. But it would become much worse at half-time when some of those bodies would be slick with sweat, spittle and nasal goo.

We were all dressed and waiting for Pechman, his son David, and coach Charley Butler to come in and take turns trying to brutalize us in the Vince Lombardi tradition. Pechman's kid is 12 years old and Pechman actually tried to change the name of the team to the Wellington "Davids" last year— but the rules committee turned Pechman down on the grounds that the move was too shabby and detrimental to the APBA's image, and it couldn't guarantee an immediate cash return. David, who is a miniature of a 50-year-old businessman on the wrong side of a stroke, was inconsolable for the rest of the season. Papa P. seems to have made the little urchin happy again by naming him the official team mascot and putting his beaming face on the program.

A couple of players were working hard on some $3-a-gallon rosé, like they were in wino heaven, and Foot was stoking up in the john with Sandy McLean, our ball-handling guard. Why let a little thing like a playoff game spoil a good time?

A polite tap on the door reminded everybody to put their fixings away until half-time. David, in a pin-striped suit and black tie, scampered in first. Lyndon King, the worst player on the team and a starting forward, ruffled his hair and straightened his clip-on tie . . . while Pechman smiled paternally and Lacey mumbled obediently.

Arnold Pechman had married his money and was the prestigious owner of Wellington's only glitter-chic clothing store, "The Greatest Gatsby." The ultra-fine threads in the window were taken home by a handful of young execs who had moved here from New York two years ago when ITT had relocated one of its computer-components plants. On sale in the rear

28

room—where French postcards are usually sold to drooling old men—was a collection of cheap overalls, mackinaws and work clothing. The back room paid the rent, but Pechman was planning to use the playoff gate receipts to construct a back entrance off the rear alley. He figured that David Bowie would never buy his spangles in the same place where coal miners buy thermal underwear.

No matter what clothing Pechman wore, his belly put creases where they didn't belong. Beau Pechman was also a jock sniffer of such intensity that his nose looked like a nigger's cock—and how he loved to jive the brothers. Clarence and me had to call him "Mr. Pechman" while the rest of the guys called him "Arnold."

Pechman saw himself as a Jewish soul brother in a frigid, Gentile rube-town. He was more than slightly resentful that the citizens of Wellington didn't appreciate the glamor and class that he had imported to their city—but for the right price, we gave him all the appreciation he could handle. Actually, Pechman wasn't a bad guy, it's just that my eyeballs got greasy whenever I looked at him.

Standing with his hands on his hips and his weight athletically shifted to one leg, Arnold Pechman delivered the inspirational words which were supposed to fire us to a mean, competitive edge: "You guys know how big this game is . . . it's the nitty gritty of the season. All of . . . ahm . . . you . . . have worked hard all year and this series is the . . . a . . . culmination of . . . ahm . . . a lot of hard work. So go out there . . . and win."

Coach Butler was next—he brushed his hand over his cannon-bald head and did a Knute Rockne that we all could relate to. "Just do me a favor," he said, "and play this game like it's a road game. And remember . . ." He held his thumb and fore-finger two inches apart. ". . . you're only this far away from big-league pussy."

There was, as usual, a full house of some 2500 kings and queens of the blast furnace. The fans around the league are interchangeable—bitter, tight-faced people who break out of their bleak lives by going totally beserk at APBA ballgames. If the vendors ever ran out of beer, they would tear the place to the ground.

The women are by far the worst—with their kerchiefs around their heads, their shapeless housedresses and their big brown shoes. Their voices always manage to slice through the coarse beer rumblings of their husbands and the abuse they scream at us is the best education that David Pechman is ever going to get. The really scary thing, though, is that there is always an underlying tremor of violence pouring out of the stands in any given league game. And tonight the Beast's eyes were red with blood—10 white-uniformed washed-out mercenaries were being entrusted with the honor of defending the Wellingtonian communal cave. If we wouldn't take care of business, they would come charging out of their bleacher seats to protect their women, children and virgin daughters themselves.

The crowd around the Miners' basket was unloading on Drew "Rubber" Simonds. Rubber was the league's top scorer, doing it at 47 and change per game—but he thought "defense" was when a chick kicked a rapist in the balls. Rubber's main claim to immortality was a christening that was the stuff of which legends are made:

The worst thing that can happen to a great shooter is to have one of his shots blocked, and the name "Rubber" goes back to a famous incident in a playground in Greenwich Village. It seems that Simonds foolishly decided to go up and challenge Kareem Abdul-Jabbar, who not only rejected the shot but sent it flying over the fence and bouncing onto Sixth Avenue, where a city bus ran over the ball. Someone retrieved the mashed ball and handed it to Simonds. "Here you go, sucker," he said. "Take this poor ol' rubber on home and wear it on your head when it rains." But Jabbar doesn't play in the APBA and there are no buses in Wellington, so Rubber doesn't have to look over his shoulder when he shoots.

Meanwhile, at our end of the court, Foot was inciting the crowd with some highly imaginative dunking. You could see the charge blow out their black lungs when he jammed one backwards. While all of this exhibitionism was going on, I happened to cast an admiring eye in the direction of Rubber's amazo corkscrew jumpers—the man shoots like a saint! And I saw one of the Miners standing with his arms folded, not bothering to take any practice shots. It was Tarzan Cooper grimacing with pain and kinetic evil every time Foothead threw one down.

The American Legion Glee Club did a howling a cappella National Anthem and we were ready to play. The Rifles opened with Foot in the middle, Lacey and McLean at guard and King and Wilfred up front. The Miners started TC at center, Rubber and Brennan in the backcourt, and Cody Wells and a skinny white dude name of Middleton at the fowards. Tarzan went after Foot as soon as the official threw the ball up to start the game, catching him on the shoulder with a forearm, but the ref on top of the play was too busy watching the ball to see it.

The outcome of the game itself was decided on the very first play—Foot had enough balance left to tap the ball to Wilfred, who dribbled straight to the basket, put Brennan on his ass, and scored the easy lay-up. Even though Brennan had been parked in the lane long before Will busted him to the floor, Artie was charged with a blocking foul. We were 15 to 20 points better than the Blues anyway, but the call made it clear that the officials didn't plan on battling their way to their cars after the game was over. Everybody quickly read the handwriting on the scoreboard and spent the next couple of hours trying to do two things—score as many points as possible and totally avoid any body contact.

The first part was easy—in a "real" basketball game when one team takes an insurmountable lead, everybody goes crazy hoisting everything up but the lines on the floor. You could play with five basketballs at the same time and none of the players would know the difference—it's called "garbage time." After Wilfred's 3-point play, "atomic waste" set in. No one on either team wanted to inbound the ball. When the Blues scored, everybody but Foot vanished—if an assist is the last pass leading to a basket, then Foot's total would put Tiny Archibald to shame. The only other passes that were made were the under-the-asshole variety, the kind that caused dancing in the streets on Sixth Avenue. Wellington fans responded with loud "Yahoooos!" The score at the quarter was 42 to 28.

Normally, staying healthy was just as easy—defense was "Hurry up and score so I can score." A couple of waves with the hand as the bull charged to the basket was entirely sufficient. But that night Tarzan was on the prowl.

He was not only setting picks, he was giving that little wriggle just before contact that loosened the pickee's fillings and untied his shoelaces. Once around the team was enough to convince one and all that a wary charting of TC's movements was necessary for personal survival. And when Tarzan came down with a rebound his elbows shed people like a dog shaking off the rain.

Five minutes into the game, Foot was the only player who was coming close enough to Tarzan to be hit. Foot was either very numb or very brave and he spent a lot of time peeling himself off the floor. Near the end of the quarter, TC almost got Foot's nose. To a big man, inflicting a broken nose is the same as a matador being awarded a tail, two ears and a pair of balls.

The next 12 minutes featured more of the same—Wilfred scoring lay-ups and getting "fouled," Rubber radaring 20-footers whenever he got the ball, Sandy dancing passes off of teammates' heads and Lacey running around looking suave. But like a black Moby Dick, the presence of Tarzan Cooper hulked over the entire game. The beating he dealt to Foot-head was almost wondrous in its complexity and its intensity. And stringy old Foothead Jones, his skull bursting with meta-physical picks and rolls, said nothing. One loud complaint to an official would have at least put some serious foul trouble on TC, one look of outrage would have moved the Beast to demand that justice be visited upon one of their favorite niggers—but Foot simply went about his basketball business and the carnage continued.

I was scared shitless watching all of this from the bench—if Foot really got maimed, my very own personal pink ass would be next on the block.

During a time-out I asked Lacey if he knew why Foot was offering himself so meekly. "You go ask him your own self," Lacey said. "But if the man can't shoot, and can't handle, he got to earn his money doin' sompthin'."

We led 81-63 at the half and the virginal trickle of sweat on my forehead was produced by rescuing Foot's warm-up jacket from a fan as we left the bench and headed for the locker room. Maybe he just wanted a sacred relic of the first martyr the game of basketball was ever going to produce.

We were settling down inside the tiny room when Charley Butler stuck his face inside the door.

"Foot, you okay?"

A Cheshire nod from the middle of a sweaty haze.

"Okay," Charley said. "I'll come get you in fifteen minutes." And he locked the door from the outside. The wine, booze and grass were hustled out and the half-time show began. While Lacey and Will conducted a revivalist review of the first half's missed shots and unmade passes, I sidled my chair over to where Foot was getting peacefully restoned.

"Hey, rookie," he said cheerfully. "Take a pull, it's from the good side of some ol' Colombian hill."

It was sweeter than the stuff we had smoked in the car and, as it turned out, much more potent. We sat quietly for a while, letting the smoke ring its way around our heads. From where I sat I could see Lacey and Wilfred hopping about the room and squawking like a pair of gigantic magpies.

"Man," Heckle clacked in the middle of a hysterical grand mal, "you dudes see how I rejected that nigger Cody's shit?"

"Sure did," Jeckle slapped his knee. "He almost ate a Wilson burger."

All the birds erupted into a chorus of raucous laughter. I silenced them by turning to Foothead.

"Wacky weed," I said.

"Ain' nothin' but . . ."

I felt an overpowering empathy for this strangely elongated and strangely attired man from nowhere—this upsidedown philosopher with a number on his back and a pair of sneakers on his hands. The weed had me in a very silly mood and I thought I'd see if I could put him on a little.

34

"Old Foothead," I began. "Speak to me in hound dog tongues . . ."

"You a good kid, rookie," he said without a smile. "But you too young and too light up side yo' head. This ain' the place and it ain' the time for bullshittin'."

The two magpies were doing a jive pantomime and Foot's little crackly voice was the only sound I could hear. And I didn't feel silly any more.

I was pretty high throughout the rest of the game, and I tried to hide behind Clarence at the end of the bench. Tarzan picked up his fifth foul at the beginning of the last quarter, but when a sub was honked into the game, TC waved him away and refused to come out. I don't think I had ever rooted for anyone to foul out of a game before but I was sure doing it then.

The Miners were losing by 35 and Tarzan was about as frustrated as he could be. The only satisfaction left for him was to shut Lacey's face—at one point TC tiptoed up to the mid-court line to set a pick for Rubber, but Lacey felt the hot bronco breath on the back of his neck and to avoid getting hit he made a deliberately wild, dividing swipe in the general direction of the ball. Rubber wound up with a lay-up (an open 15-foot jumper) and Lacey wound up on the floor snapping his fingers in dismay—and the Wellington fans stood and applauded Lacey's "hustle." For once in their basketball lives, the fans were right.

With just 5 minutes to go, Charley started to clear the bench—that meant me. My head was still light and goofy when I threw Foot his jacket and asked him who he was guarding.

Brennan was shooting a free throw, so I took one of the inside spots along the lane. My job would be to put my body in between the basket and Tarzan, who was on my right—the idea was to keep him off the boards. But before Brennan released the ball, TC hooked my shoulder with his left elbow and then planted a forearm on my chest. I couldn't believe the pain. It felt like somebody hit me in the heart with an axe. There was no foul called, the officials wanted to get home as quickly as everybody else did.

While I was on the floor Clarence hit a lay-up and the Miners came charging back on offense. I took a tentative step to see if my body still worked, and saw Tarzan breaking out of the pack with the ball—only he was looking at me, not at the basket. In the John Wooden Handbook, the X is supposed to hold his position and draw a charging foul on the O. Every drill I had done in my life, every competitive instinct I had, told me not to move, to make the righteous play. I tried to speak, to tell TC to stop. I put my hand on my chest to move him to compassion, to remind him how much he had hurt me moments before—but he kept coming. And I said, "Fuck you, Red Holzman," and I ran out of bounds.

Most of the crowd was either gone or in the process of going, but a few people booed—and when I hit a classic high-arching 20-footer at the buzzer there was only a mumble of general approval from a few stragglers.

Wilfred had something going, so only me, Lacey and Foot drove back. Foot beat me to the back seat and slept all the way to the New Jersey Turnpike. It was a sacred tradition that the man riding shotgun had to stay awake and keep Lacey company, but my chest was hurting me too much to sleep anyway. Lacey babbled about this pass and that shot, and did I see the ugly that Will was with and how about when he stuck one in Rubber's face and . . . I mumbled "Yes" and "Uh-huh" while my body throbbed and the highway melted in front of us.

Foothead did wake up once—it was while we were gassing up in Easton and Lacey had gone to get some cigarettes. "Hey, rookie," he said wearily.

"Yeah, Foot."

"You just got to decide if you a big man or a little man." And he shifted position and was gone again.

MINERS				RIFLES			
	FG	FT	P		FG	FT	P
Simonds	20	1-1	41	Jones	5	2-9	12
Brennan	12	3-5	25	Freeman	15	9-10	39
Cooper	13	2-6	28	McLean	6	7-10	19
Wells	8	2-2	18	King	6	4-4	16
Middleton	6	0-1	12	Williams	18	21-24	57
Johnson	2	1-1	5	Fitzgerald	3	1-1	7
Hamilton	1	0-0	2	Lassner	1	0-0	2
Daniels	3	1-2	7	Paterson	2	0-1	4
				Wilson	0	2-2	2
				Mathews	1	0-0	2

MINERS	28	35	32	43 —	138
RIFLES	42	39	40	49 —	170

TIME OUT

We are living in a very dangerous universe—every parsec, every street corner is teeming with exploding galaxies, stray bullets, renegade comets, falling debris, homicidal maniacs and drunken drivers. The awareness that any one of an infinite number of hazards could step on my life was an absolute terror to me. And the thought of my consciousness being painfully condensed into the void of black space and hollow time was totally oppressive. I firmly believed that the object of life was to avoid death.

My father was 43 going on one hundred when he died. He was a very sickly man who, at various times in his life, was inflicted with tuberculosis, heart disease, kidney ailments, asthma and diabetes. Next to his bed was a gray torpedo of oxygen which he gulped and sucked at whenever his one remaining lung was overtaxed. I used to lie in bed with my pillow stuffed into my ears trying to shut out the hissing sound that meant he would live until at least the morning.

He was a brilliant man—an unschooled sewing-machine operator who spent his invalid years devouring whole libraries and corresponding with novelists, political columnists and anyone else who lived "out there" and who bothered to answer his letters. Nelson Algren, I remember, wrote him at least one letter, as did Max Lerner.

I found out after he died that my father had been a Party member in the 30s—I wish I could have seen him arguing the proper "Path" with his cronies over rye bread, bowls of borscht and pamphlets ... But I was the doltish son who wasted his time playing ballgames and who was only good for ferrying books into and out of every public library within reach of public transportation. My mother's younger brother, Richard, was selected as his spiritual heir. Even though he was regaled with brilliant conversation and primed with the proper reading matter, Richard turned out to be a beer-swilling fireman who married a witless, malleable girl from Brooklyn. But all of this was after my father died.

His maladies turned my father sullen, then bitter and finally vicious. I was a helpless hulk when I was a kid and I remember coming home from one of my weekly street beatings—my mother was still at work and my father was in his bed reading a book on astronomy that I had fetched for him that morning. When I came in crying, he angrily told me to keep quiet and not to bother him. But I was eleven years old and I hurt, so I kept on whimpering. He became enraged and he reached under his bed for the bottle which he used during the day to avoid making the painful journey through the living room and down the foyer to the bathroom. Without uttering a word, he hurled the half-full bottle to where I was crouched on the floor. It crashed against my forehead, soaking my whole body with blood and stale paternal urine. I ran out of the apartment and into the street where a neighbor found me and took me to the hospital to be stitched up. The incident was never mentioned again—I told my mother that I had fallen in the playground.

My father died three years later, succumbing to an attack of something painful and slow. I accompanied my mother in the ambulance, and just before we reached the hospital, my father opened his eyes. I remember that his pupils were tightly clenched with the agony of dying. He looked, I thought, at the scar on my forehead. "Hi, kid," is what he said before he closed his eyes, farted and then died for the last time.

The rabbi began the funeral services by telling all the mourners how wonderful we all were for showing up so early on a Sunday morning. We were scoring points and God would surely reward us by lengthening our days and joys (a redundancy I did not fail to register). My father was a "blade of grass in the field of humanity, giving nourishment and support for the trees and flowers which everyone sees and admires." Then he chanted in Hebrew—the only words I could understand were "International Ladies Garment Workers Union." But the message was clear—better to live in shit up to your eyebrows than to be buried in a gold coffin.

So . . . I carefully closed all my covers before striking after that. I avoided lawn mowers and noncarbonated orange drinks . . . I locked up the living me inside of my huge and well-fortified body. Sending out a trendril of compassion, commitment or even passionate interest was to risk amputation and lessen the odds on surviving. I pumped my soul full of acute observations and the most subjective of judgments.

I dreamed of the perfect life—sitting in a contour chair, watching an incredibly detailed movie of my own life. With my fingers on the "Reverse" and the "Freeze" buttons. My friends had to drag me to social gatherings . . . and I never really enjoyed myself. I anxiously bided my time until I returned to the Loew's Lassner and turned on the projector to watch myself at the party, dance, dinner, etc.

I was almost shamed into playing basketball—it was a way of putting an end to the beating I had been catching. I never forgot that the ancient Mexicans played a ball game with a strange name—and the loser was executed. In spite of myself, playing basketball grew to be fun. I did have some natural abilities—my jump shot, for example. But I never really leveled—failure is easy to live with when Doctor Faustus insists that you could have done better had you wanted to do so.

My sophomore year at Hunter was a trial—I didn't know the other teams, the other players. I didn't know how much effort was necessary to avoid being embarrassed. I learned the answer quickly: Not much.

The third game of that year I fielded a stray elbow with my mouth and I was overjoyed. I had paid my "dues," I had made a sacrificial offering in order to perpetuate the illusion that I was actively participating and it hadn't hurt—nor had it diminished me in any way. The school paid for a gold inlaid false tooth, one that would never fall out or need a filling.

Being a second-string center in a gadget like the APBA *seemed* like the perfect place to go through the motions . . . But I was afraid that Tarzan Cooper wanted more than just a tooth.

CHAPTER THREE

I DIDN'T WANT TO SUB ON MONDAY so before I went to bed I yanked the phone out of the wall jack. It cost me $30 to have that fucken gismo installed, but I love the idea of being able to unplug myself from the computer. I would consider it sufficient proof of the existence of God if it turns out that the phone jack was made in ITT's Wellington factory.

I didn't sleep too well anyway—Tarzan had added at least two red and painful inches to the width of my sternum and it throbbed like a bastard everytime I moved. So I followed the advice of Dr. Kronkite: for most of the day I didn't move. Gus had left a greasy chunk of Polish sausage in the refrigerator and there was still a drop of Boone's Farm Apple Wine, so I didn't even have to go out for eats.

Gus Zovitowski is the name of the other stooge that our landlady swindles for $90 every month. (Ziva Zahavy is the chick's name, by the way. She's an immigrant from somewhere in Eastern Europe who sold a cab driver the Brooklyn Bridge the minute she got off the boat. But she's sort of laid back in her own very intense sort of way.) The rent pays for separate bedrooms, a large room containing a foam-rubber couch like the kind used as lounges in the offices of cheap motels, a bridge table with four hideous but very sturdy chairs and some assorted kitchen equipment. As a bonus for paying cash, Mrs. Zahavy cleans the place every 2 weeks and because my unbelievable sloth so offends her Lysolian sensibilities, she

42

also washes the accumulated dishes—Gus lives on White Castle hamburgers. Gus was already living there when Madame Zahavy showed me the apartment, but it was obvious that he was a gentle soul and, besides, the bathroom had a magnificent stall shower. After spending my formative years carefully washing and rinsing my body so as not to splash any water between the plastic curtains and onto the floor, I was a chump for the pebbled, translucent shower door.

Another reason why I grabbed at the chance to live here is that my poor widowed mother was beginning to tie my entire nervous system into a ball of string with a "Holy Martyr" routine she has been perfecting over the years—so I was saying "Yes" from the minute Mrs. Zahavy opened the door. The basement apartment was also, I am ashamed to admit, a perfect 10 blocks from my mother's three and a half rooms, far enough to keep her away and close enough to freebie a pot-roast dinner once a week. Sometimes I think that this is, indeed, the best of all possible worlds.

I also lucked out with Gus. He is a 38-year-old unhappily married Catholic—a parlay nobody ever really beats. I've taken messages from the permanent Mrs. Gustaf Zovitowski on the phone and she sounds like the Queen of the Red Hot Harpies. I keep telling Gus he should split to Idaho or someplace, but he has two teenage daughters—a brace of wimp-faced defensive tacklettes named Katrina and Palinka—so Gus's fast break to freedom turned out to be moving to the Bronx and sending his wife half his check every week.

We stay out of each other's way for the most part but sometimes when Gus comes home drunk and I'm ripped enough we do manage to talk through the wire screen. He usually shrugs and stammers his problems at me while I cluck sympathetically and console him with an occasional "There,

43

there." About the most perceptive thing Gus comes up with is "You single guys have it made." The poor fucker—he's like a big bozo puppy who'll lick his master's boots no matter how many times he's been kicked. But one of the best things about having Gus as a roommate is that he spends most of his free time at a Polish version of the Mystic Knights of the Sea Lodge Hall located near City Island.

At about six o'clock I had enough of being electronically nonexistent so I reconnected the phone and sat staring at it waiting for the memory bank to tell me something I could use. But Gus interrupted my vigil—as he opened the front door and saw me sitting there on the couch, his wide face split into an even wider smile.

"Hi, Bo," he said. "Did you guys win?"

"Sure, no trouble."

Gus didn't know enough about basketball to ask how many points I had scored or if I had gotten laid down in Wellington. But he was genuinely delighted to discover that the Rifles had defeated the Elizabeth Miners—and that delighted me as well.

"You going to the club tonight? Or you want to go get a pizza or something?"

I had been living there for nearly 7 months and we had never eaten dinner together, but I was feeling as though there was some kind of spiritual plug dangling freely and I wanted some real company after my heavy Sunday. Gus, however, was already changing into his beige chino pants and gray V-neck sweater—his "Kingfishovski" outfit.

"Sorry, kid," he said. "We've got a council meeting . . . to plan our spring trip to Bear Mountain. All we have to do is charter a couple of buses, buy a few kegs of beer and tell the women to cook up some food . . . but we'll all get drunk and it'll take us the whole night to work out the details."

"Sounds like fun," I said, trying to fake some enthusiasm.

"Yeah . . . it's as good an excuse as any to tie one on. Well . . . see you later."

"So long, Gus."

He left the *Times* for me, so I had at least a half hour's reprieve before I was forced to turn on the TV. But midway through the sports section, the phone rang. My "savior" turned out to be an ex-college teammate with an extra ticket to a rock concert. Why not? What the fuck?

The guy's name was Marty Kaplan and he showed up at 11:00 with the tickets, some mescaline, his car and a plastic chick named Diane Greenbaum-berg-ski-farb-trowitz. That immediately meant that the Chick-Fuck-Wife alert was cancelled for the evening. Which was fine with me—my body hurt too much to try and do anything with it anyway.

Marty used to live where I used to live and we wasted our alloted portion of time together. Since the both of us had graduated and moved, we'd both found other ways to do the same thing and the only circumstances that got us together anymore occurred four or five times a year when Marty came up with an extra ticket to a rock concert. But we still had our little ritual thing going, and Diane looked like soft plastic at least . . . and Marty did have those three lovely doses of what he called "super-good mesc."

I used to enjoy seeing a good rock band playing the Fillmore. When a group like the Dead or the Airplane were on the bill, every phylum of raggedy freak, Pavement Farmer and Central Park free spirit would attend an evening-long prayer meeting of the Fillmore Fraternal Acid Blast and Marching Society. The instant the music stopped we would revert into our private brain-rotting fantasies, but as long as the man with the guitar was preaching, there were 2500 hippies all bearing witness to electric love and psychedelic brotherhood. It was better than watching "Let's Make a Deal" and we all were convinced that the whole scene provided a necessary element of purity and togetherness in our lives. The passing of a couple of years has dimmed out the memories of the bummer acid, the downed-out ushers gleefully stomping on their more rowdy brothers, and the whole phoney carnival, so I guess I still have the same holes in my soul as I did then.

What I am also missing is the tolerance needed to stand on a fucken line for two hours with a bunch of tailored street people and Qualuuded glitter-boppers—but Marty insisted that the "stoned scene" was an important part of the floor show. There were some familiar faces and bodies in attendance, however. There was Charley the Clown walking his invisible dog—the petting and scratching of which was still accepted as an absolute sign of uncorrupted innocence. The seven-foot Dead head was making the rounds still looking like a bizarro Johnnie Winters. I once looked into his eyes to see if he was a functioning basketball player, but all I saw were the dusty remains of some psychedelic ghost town. And a gaggle of flannel-shirted earth mothers from Brooklyn were also there, chanting their liberated Om: "Any extra tickets? A blow job for an extra ticket." I always wondered if the payment was any different for an orchestra seat than for one in the balcony.

The resident brother blood had also made an appearance—we used to call him Nephew Thomas. He swore up, down and sideways that he just loved to bugaloo to that good old rock and roll, but his sloe-eyed horniness burrowed its way into the panties of every cutie who looked at him and didn't see a black man.

But these people were the familiar Dramatis Personnae of my personal movie—it was the extras from the wardrobe department who bothered me. Somewhere there are machines which do nothing but wear holes into new blue jeans. And the next stop on the assembly line is manned by old ladies sewing patches and dripping grease on strategic spots. A few walk-ons were sporting platform shoes and sequined faces. Mass-produced raunchiness or computer-designed decadence—one uniform or another.

The line was starting to move—this was Marty's cue to flourish his little pillbox filled with foil-wrapped mescaline tabs.

"You want to drop now?" he asked me. "Or you want to wait till we're inside? It's a little speedy, so I think we should do it now."

To trip or not to trip . . . to do a one-and-a-half gainer into the cesspool of my subconscious and let it corrode away all the suet on the inside of my head. But what will happen when Mental Hernia turns on the smoke machine and starts to smash their guitars. What will happen when my head opens up and finds itself in the middle of screeching Beatle-mania and the Beatles aren't there?

"Uh . . . Marty . . . you know something? I just remembered that I left the water running in the bathroom sink."

"What the fuck are you raving about?" But his outrage quickly turned into a smile. He poked Diane confidentially and gave her a winking aside. "I told you that stuff we did in the car was good. Look how stoned he is."

They both giggled. I had to get the fuck out of there immediately.

"No . . . I'm not kidding. There's going to be a flood. I'll . . . I'll call you tomorrow. Nice to meet you, Diane."

Embarrassed at telling such a ridiculous story, I wheeled around quickly and headed toward the subway . . . the pain in my chest had increased noticeably.

A chick in a red-flannel shirt hit me with a moving pick. "Hey, man. You got an extra ticket, right?"

"As a matter of fact, yeah."

"Outasight . . . there's a doorway over there . . ."

"No, no," I said. "You see that black dude over there? Here's the ticket . . . now go and lay your trip on him. Okay?"

"Sure, man. A ticket's a ticket."

There was no chance that I'd be able to get up and sub Tuesday morning, so before I surrendered to the subway I jumped into the Bookmasters on the same corner. I hereby affirm and declare that books are a minority which have been significantly discriminated against. And, therefore, in the interest of fostering understanding among God's creatures, I've made an unswerving practice of rescuing my hardcovered brothers from a variety of cruel masters, from the inhuman concentration camps presided over by the New York Public Library, and from the horrifying slave auctions held at bookstores all over the city. As I reassured a copy of Marlowe's *The Tragical History of Doctor Faustus* that I was working on his behalf, I became aware of a pair of suspicious eyes diagramming my every move in a huge, concave mirror suspended from the ceiling.

It was the chick who was chained to the cash register for $2.75 an hour. I threw an indignant face at the mirror and as soon as she got embarrassed enough to look away I deposited the book in my coat pocket. After visiting more of my little friends and whispering promises of deliverance to *The Idiot* and *Miss Lonelyhearts*, I slinked inconspicuously toward the exit.

"Excuse me, sir." It was the cashier again.

"You're excused," I said without slowing down. But she did a Houdini, popped out from behind her machine and nagged at my sleeve.

"Hey, man. You don't want to get busted for lifting a 95-cent paperback . . ."

"Me? Busted? Paperback?" A tidal wave of innocence, outrage and persecution came pouring out of my baby blues.

"Don't give me that bullshit," she snapped. "Just put the God-damned thing back on the shelf and get the fuck out of here."

Surprise! Surprise! I could see the cluster of freckles around her nose flickering with anger. She had crisp, straw-brown hair and her gray eyes were set just a freckle and a half too wide apart—but they beaconed a faunlike sexuality which seemed incongruous when paired with the slightness of her body. I was positive that she made a dynamite brown-rice casserole and that her favorite poet was William Blake.

"Okay. Okay. Take it easy," I said. "If you tell me your name, I'll put the book back."

She tried to maintain the edge of her anger but a brown-red flush forced her to smile. "Rachael."

"Hey, listen," I said with an outstretched hand vouching for my sincerity. "I don't mean to cause any trouble . . . but it's a good book . . . see? And I really don't have any money . . . I was going to give it a real good home. Honest."

Her shoulders slumped a little and the tension eased from her face. "Okay . . . I'm sorry I jumped all over you. When you spend eight hours a day in here hassling all the creeps trying to swipe copies of *SCREW* and all that other porno shit . . . it just makes you jumpy. Leave the book here, I'll put it away later."

Rachael in the alien corn? . . . or dancing with some dude's head? . . . or something like that. Radiance and tragedy in an all-night bookstore. I couldn't find the slightest excuse for not falling in love.

I decided on a Humphrey Bogart–cum–Woody Allen exit. I sucked my front teeth and twitched my cheeks. "You're a nice chick."

There was no change in her soft smile or in the well of her eyes as she answered me—no challenge, no close-out, but no weakness either.

"I'm no chick," she said. "I'm a woman."

The D train took an hour and a half to get me back to the Bronx, and I believe I smiled all the way.

SECOND QUARTER

CHAPTER **F**OUR

I COULDN'T FACE UP TO SUBBING until Wednesday, so I left the phone plugged in Tuesday night. Gus tripped out at his usual 7 sharp and he snapped my eyes open when he accidentally slammed the door. There was only one thing I could do—get up, take the phone out and go back to sleep. But I felt guilty as shit when I awoke, so I immediately lit up a joint.

It was no use. In between sexual fantasies, Jiminy Cricket was out debating Faustus and I was a goner. Mephistopheles had run fresh out of Helen of Troy's anyway—so I decided I would definitely go in on Thursday. And good old Jiminy laid out all the necessary justifications:

a) I needed the $49,
b) Substituting for a gym teacher was not at all like working,
c) I needed the run to keep my game sharp,
d) All the kids at Ryder J.H.S. know that I play in the APBA, so I'd get a lot of courtesy from them and they wouldn't bust my balls too much,
e) If I didn't answer the fucken phone at least one morning a week they would stop calling me,
f) If they ever did that, I'd have to drive a fucken cab after the playoffs,
g) Or move back in with my mother,

h)   The pain in my chest had subsided to the point where
      the axe wound had healed and my entire body was
      merely throbbing like a 225-pound heart with
      gummy rings and a sticky valve.

But when the phone rang the next morning, Jiminy had cut
out and the loyal Doctor F. shrieked in agony.

As seen from the "el" platform, the school appears as a
massive, ominous castle under heavy seige. The surrounding
territory has been blasted with boarded-up tenements,
stripped and burned-out cars and the total fallout of beer cans
and broken glass—but the black infidels will not retreat. The
South Bronx is a "new" ghetto without the identity or organ-
ization that the more-established areas like Bed-Stuy and
Harlem have evolved. There are no clearly defined front lines
here, so a kind of anarchic guerrilla warfare is the primary
tactic—and no-man's-land is everywhere.

The enemy hordes have managed some tentative inroads
into the minor bureaucracy which governs the feudal palace
—a gym teacher, the Dean of Boys, the entire custodial staff
and a couple of Guidance Department paper pushers. Par-
tially because of this infiltration, the forbidding outer gates no
longer intimidate the peasants and it is only a matter of time
and Civil Service erosion until this particular monument to
Western brainpower becomes an Easter Island of ruined
stone.

The Baron has all but abdicated already—he spends most of
his time writing reports and hiding behind the desk in his
chambers. Saul Solomon is the principal's name and with two
names like that he must have some nigger blood struggling
through his varicose veins. He's been at Ryder Junior High
School for nearly 35 years and he can't understand where all

the bright-eyed, studious and properly humble little Jewish boys and girls have gone. When the weekly rumble takes place in the schoolyard, Solomon takes the phone off the hook, closes the door to his office and while he watches for a grappling hook to come crashing through his window he prays that the "schwarzers" will all kill each other.

On the 4th floor, the Boys Gymnasium makes the Rifles' home court look like Madison Square Garden—but it is also the site of the major pocket of enemy occupation within the school. It is here that they worship one of their pagan gods—Basketball Jones. Because of my magic jump shot I am fully accepted as an honorary priest. Being a teacher in this sanctum sanctorum means blowing on your whistle a lot, instructing the obviously corrupt monitors to take attendance, and throwing out the basketballs.

There is supposed to be a regulation gym uniform of red shorts and a red shirt, but anything vaguely suggestive of this livery is considered acceptable—red sneaker laces, red wrist bands, a pair of bloodshot eyes, or even a severely bleeding wound. Converse sneakers are the standard, but the observing eye can find Space Flyers, Sky Hoppers and others of the same Johns Bargain Store ilk. The shorts exhibit a similar variety, but most of them are framed by the gravitationally inspired unfolding of some very fancy boxer drawers. Some of the kids wear shirts from night-center leagues, some wear none at all, and some have used crayons and Magic Markers to create their own personalized jerseys—there are several "Clydes," "Dr. J.'s" and "Tinys." Every one of these kids would rather be Earl Monroe or Connie Hawkins than the President.

Maybe it's because young blacks generally believe in people who are still alive, while white folk persist in worshiping the decomposing Kennedys, "Honest Abe" Lincoln, Humphrey Bogart, Jimi Hendrix and others on the nether side of the grave. I guess it's safer to deposit one's faith in the moldy hands of a dead man—he'll never disappoint you.

It's tough for me to play ball with the kids here—they feel that it's the mark of an empty jockstrap to use a pick or to box out under the boards. Burn-on-burn is the ghetto game. Instead of the size of your car representing the length of your prick, a devastating, ego-withering move serves the very same purpose.

There's one kid named Bassett I've been trying to work with, but he has an aversion to taking a wide-open shot. He'll diddle around with the ball until a defensive man picks up on him. When I asked him about it, he said, "Man, I need a face to shoot on."

And if they find themselves all alone under the hoop, they'll crank up two or three leftover moves to try and fake out the backboard. But it's their game, and the only means of defining themselves without stealing anything or killing anybody. And these kids can really play ball—I mean they can stick you, slick you and strip you—and tie your shoelaces together at the same time. Maybe one or two of them will get some decent coaching, but most will wind up strung out on something they won't ever be able to grab hold of and their kids'll be here doing the same thing 20 years from now. It's hard not to get involved with them and try to teach them everything I know—but the playground game is the only one where any of them keep score. But Bassett is a bright kid—maybe I can do something with him. Or maybe I should mind my own fucken business.

Basketball is the black Doomsday weapon—the niggers will jive, juke, head-fake and dribble their way to the turret, the vault, the bedroom, and they already work in the castle's boiler room. *Rucker uber alles!*

But Basketball Jones, with his cosmic jumper that never ripples the cords, also demands his sacrifices. His initiates develop an abbreviated sense of humanity—the worth of an individual's soul comes to be equated with his athletic ability. And I am hip whereof I speak—I was a clod with Keds when I was a kid. I couldn't clap my hands or pick my nose without spraining something. And on those mystically rare occasions when I was chosen into a basketball game, my easily jammed fingers fortunately never got near the ball. It became increasingly difficult, as the games wore on, to tell if I was playing defense or offense—and nobody cared as long as I didn't fall on any of them. I was a victim of the rawest kind of ego-power —either you were the "greatest" or you were the "worst." It was a simple time in which to live, but a dangerous time in which to grow up. In order to keep my budding self-respect from forming a spore I had to smoke the biggest cigars in the back of Oscar's candy store and tell the biggest lies about sniffing my older sister's bras and panties. But none of this ever provided compensation enough. I never earned more than half a vote in deciding what we would do on a winter's Saturday morning—whether to catch the newest Gidget movie, steal Chinese apples from the stands on Bathgate Avenue, or try to spit against the wind from the George Washington Bridge.

My social status improved only after my body began to elongate when I reached 15—and I graduated to a vote and a half when my wrists suddenly developed the spring and touch necessary for being a good shooter. All you fat, sloppy kiddies out there can pick up an extra vote in the Bullies Local #118 by doing the same exercises that made me a success— spend large portions of your shitting time holding any Christmas issue of *Playboy* magazine at arm's length with your left hand while merry-fisting with your right hand. And developing perfect body control is a bonus, a result of the continuous effort needed to keep from falling off the toilet bowl.

Every 50 minutes a special pia mater penetrating buzz tone is beamed throughout the school, informing all the peasants that the Baron still has a button he can push. The day after a rumble, the tone usually lasts for an extra 15 seconds, making everyone feel like Winston Smith strapped to his pain-o-meter.

I stayed in the gym all day, sending the most raggedy kid I could find out for a ham and cheese hero and tipping him 50 cents—and thereby doing more for the Revolution than any of Abbie Hoffman's media rantings and ravings. But the kid fucked up the order, he came back with mayonnaise instead of mustard on the sandwich—maybe he's a double agent. I spent my free hour running wind sprints and working the stiffness out of my jump shot. I didn't want to have to deal with anybody who wasn't wearing a pair of sneakers.

Once or twice I checked out the locker room to make sure that none of the kids had fallen out from sniffing glue or snorting Boraxo. Not that I really gave a shit, but I just wanted them to see my face down there and remember that the whistle around my neck could turn into a whip if I was bastard enough. Only two or three kids bothered to dampen their sweaty bodies in the showers—they obviously came from apartments where hot water was something that came from tea kettles. A few of the other kids who believed that cleanliness was second only to a well-executed fast break moved closer to the godhead by taking Harlem Showers. They would pull a crusty towel from a cheap overnight bag, blot up as much sweat as possible and finish by anointing themselves with Holy Aqua Velva. But having a stylish bag is the key move in this particular Mass—"You got to have a bag, man, and it got to say Adidas on the side."

It almost goes without saying that I waited until I got home to the luxury and decadence of my very own shower stall—and while I was soaping my crotch I thought of Rachael. If there was anything wrong with her it might be that she was too "ethnic." She could possibly turn out to be one of those chicks with a super snatch who used to be recruited by the Communist Party to pussy-whip and make true believers out of whoever mosied into their beds. Nowadays these same chicks are balling for Ecology Now, Save Our Day Care Centers, and for Lever Brothers' secret toothpaste brainstorms. I really should borrow Gus' station wagon and pick up on her some night—maybe Friday.

But there was a joint lying on the dresser, and Marty came over with some coke, a few splinters of mescaline and a play-by-play of his double overtime session with Diane—and I was off on a two-day blind high. When I could function again, it was Saturday morning and I was standing on Canal Street waiting for Lacey.

CHAPTER Five

WILL HAD SPENT FRIDAY NIGHT boogeying Uptown and woogeying Downtown, so the usual detour to Jersey City was unnecessary. And the throw-in was that I wound up sharing the back seat with Foothead, while Lacey and Will traded insults and lies in the front seat.

Foot looked a little more scuffed and bent than usual—his head appeared to be at least two sizes larger than it was last weekend. Maybe the universe was pressing down too hard on him—or perhaps TC had licked him on the sole with a pile driver that I hadn't seen.

"Foot," I said as I waved off the joint he proferred, "you look like shit."

Will and Lacey stopped chattering long enough to determine that Foothead wasn't going to put any scorching abuse on either of them. But, of course, Heckle-Jeckle was disappointed that Jeckle-Heckle was also getting off without losing at least a few feathers. When they saw that they were both out of jeopardy for the time being, they tuned Foothead out and their heads began quivering again with more brain-boggling epics about all the "foxy eyes" each had fucked since last Sunday. Lacey was going on about a chick who dealt cocaine in a very unusual manner—she carried her stash around in a huge suppository which was inserted in her cunt. Lacey, naturally, had tickled her panties and had spent half the week on an incredible coke-fuck express. He was claiming that his balls were still higher than his head was.

I don't know ... at the beginning of the season I used to half-believe most of their crazy stories. Then it got to the point where I laughed at them. And finally I began to feel sorry for them—I mean it was obvious that neither Lacey nor Will believed their own fancified lies anymore. Now I guess I'm more digusted than anything else. They don't seem like real people. And besides, once they got started up again, they were yapping too fucken loud and I wanted to catch all of Foot-head's monologue.

"Rookie," he said, totally aware that I was his only listener, "we got to be real careful tonight. We one up on them an' we gonna be loosey goosey an' they gonna be tight like an ol' lady's rusty-pissy pussy. We jus' got to keep a eye steady on that sco'e bo'd an' we got to make sho' we don' sneak up on 'em. Got to be ree-al careful. Cost us some lively dollars if we win, unnerstan'? Now that nigger up there ..."

He pointed to Lacey. It was clear that Foot didn't want to be distracted or interrupted and that he was creeping up on something aimed straight at me. I began to feel a little itchy and exposed and I thought I'd try and change the subject whenever he got too close.

"That nigger cain' see Sunday fo' Sat'day night. He think if he sco'es good tonight, he get a few extree bucks from Arnol' after the game. But he don' see if he sco'es too much, he gonna do hisself outen a whole roll that ain' gonna be there if there ain' no game number five. What I'm sayin', rookie, is that ol' Foot got to do some uncommon shootin' an' shuckin' come the game tonight, jus' to make sho' things don' get out a han'. That's one stupid nigger!"

"Yeah," I clucked nervously. His beady eyes were like electrodes boring into my brain, and so his twinkling, stump-toothed smile made me feel he was about to turn on the current.

"An' you know what that mean, rookie . . ."

I surrendered my body to an empty, helpless twitch. For all I knew it meant the end of the world . . . maybe Foothead Jones was really an advance agent for some hostile alien race and the signal for total destruction was his making a 20-foot jump shot. "No," I gurgled. "I don't know what it means."

"It mean I'm gonna be puffin' an' chuggin' an' I'm gonna need me a blow now an' ag'in. An' sence the game is at 'Liz'beth, them ref'rees also gonna be lookin' extree hard an' makin' sho' I don' mess up TC's game too much."

"You mean I'll be playing a lot more than usual . . ." It was a confession, not a question.

"Now that's 'zactly right, rookie. An' it's time y'all started thinkin' 'bout why you done hopped outen Mr. TC's big ol' nasty way las' week."

"Actually," I said, "I've been worried more about the fucken pain in my chest than anything else. I mean, this crazy monster bastard came charging down on me like he wanted to kill me, and I just didn't want any part of it. It's as simple as that."

"An' don' mean nothin' else?"

"Not at all, man." I was slowly working up to an edge—but I had the feeling it was hollow inside. I cleared my throat. "Listen, Foot, basketball is played in short pants, you dig? It's nothing but a game."

Foot flapped his hands on his thighs in despair. "Ev'rythin's a game, rookie. But you ain' nothin' but a scrub. You gonna die settin' on the bench—ain' even gonna get yo' unifoam wet."

"We can't all be superstars," was my lame response.

"Games on the inside of games, rookie. Now you jus' save yo' slick ass answers fo' them two niggers up there. Jus' lissen to me good—before you start askin' a price, you got to show what you sellin'."

And he closed up his incredible electric eyes and just fell asleep in a snap.

While Foot snoozed and I stared blankly out of the window, Will was telling Lacey about three sisters he had met in Small's Paradise the other day. One was an over-ripe virgin, one was a lesbian and the other was a nymphomaniac—and Will was industriously laying out all the combinations and permutations the four of them had gone through. Lacey, of course, had a few more to suggest.

And I realized that I didn't feel sorry for either of them right then—I just felt kind of blank. I knew that something significant had happened, but I couldn't grope more than a corner of it . . . I could tell that it was windy and colorless, and that there were walls there. And, next to me, Uncle Remus snored out his buzzing, sputtering messages to Alpha Centauri.

None of the teams in the Atlantic Professional Basketball Association has a full-time trainer. The Wellington Rifles, for example, employ a physical-education major named Billy Whatsisface from nearby Bohunk Junior College to do the necessary taping. The kid is paid 75 cents an ankle and Pechman inspects the training supplies after each game to make sure that his cache of World War I surplus tape is not being wasted. Or as Pechman puts it, "You've got to keep your overhead low, or you'll find yourself in the poorhouse."

Billy is also in charge of the First Aid Kit, a corroding metal box containing a few rolls of gray, brittle adhesive tape, some gauze pads, a few loose Stars and Stripes band-aids (David is partial to them), a pencil, an enfoiliated condom, several pieces of bubble gum, and the wallets, watches and rings of the players.

A while ago, Pechman actually had the balls to try and convince us that we would be better off securing our tender extremities in Ace bandages. "They're good for you," he insisted. "They let your skin breathe." He forgot to mention that elastic wraps can be washed and used forever. And when Lacey turned an ankle in the early part of the season, Pechman was in a rage—he even threatened to fine Billy $5 for every injury that his tapings failed to prevent. But it turned out that the kid's mother was secretary to the county's Superintendent of Schools—cross her and the Rifles would be playing their home games in the Pechman driveway.

Lacey's injury uncovered another handful of spiders, grub worms and night crawlers—it revealed just how much Pechman was concerned about the health and well-being of his ballplayers, and just how badly Lacey wanted a fat wallet. Lacey hurt himself on a Saturday, and before Sunday's game in Wellington, Pechman was commiserating all over him: "Are you sure you're okay, Lace? That ankle looks pretty mean to me, maybe you'd better sit this one out. You don't want to endanger your entire career for one little ballgame. And, after all, the game is a sellout anyway. Heh, heh and heh."

But Lacey would not be moved—his "ahh-nt" and uncle had driven down from Cleveland to see him play against the Sunbury Suds and, besides, his teammates were depending on him. He couldn't let them down. So Lacey gimped around the court once or twice before sending out a semaphore for

Charley to take him out. And the hometown crowd snorted the whole shebang right up their noses—their main nigger had tried to play in pain just for them. If he had been a white man, naturally he would have played the complete game without a whimper or a whine, but they appreciated his effort and gave him a standing ovation as he hobbled to the bench. Pechman, on the other hand, was cursing Lacey, his mother's black cunt, his numerous and ill-conceived progeny and the entire continent of Africa. Under the terms of the standard APBA contract any ballplayer who suits up has to be paid in full—even if all he does is 15 seconds worth of pantomime.

So while Billy was encasing my ankles with some translucent adhesive tape, Pechman was proboscising about trying to smell out any attempt at hiding a sprain, a strain or a pedal hernia. Billy didn't have the best technique in the world—he had to tear the tape with his teeth, and he once entangled his necktie in the works, thereby causing my entire left leg to levitate when he straightened up. But the cool, wide strips weaving and tacking themselves around my shaven ankles managed to soothe me anyway. It was as though a filament of the universal tapestry was buttressing me and prompting me to try and stand erect in the cosmic wind.

Just before we were scheduled to leave the locker room, Charley Butler felt obliged to give me some additional support. Charley was a stringy 65-year-old whose white hair was still being mowed into a crew cut. There are a million Charley Butlers in America—chewy old critters with baggy gray sweatshirts that have COACH stenciled in black letters across the front, wearing faded baseball caps with R's or W's on them, and constantly fingering the crucifix-whistle that hangs from a sneaker lace around their necks. Charley had been a big-time basketball genius at Montana Southern, twice taking his teams to the NCAA finals—losing once to UCLA and then to Maryland two years later. All of Charley's ballplayers came from the ghettos of Chicago and Detroit, and he had been able to make them trust him and believe in the white man's game. When his carefully chosen studs came out to Moose Shit, Montana, they all swore that a pick and roll was something which was done to the things that lived in the upper reaches of their noses—and hitting the open man was something that happened to whites who wandered into their neighborhoods after dark. But Charley converted them, and three of his players eventually made it into the National Basketball Association.

The only trouble was that several of Charley's recruitees had never finished high school—but that was a common occurrence in major college basketball and it was merely the official reason why Charley had been canned and run out of the profession. It seems that one of Charley's players, a kid from South Chicago named Dexter Smollins, was a smack head. Other schools had offered Dexter money, chicks, cars and credit cards—Charley offered him all of this plus as much heroin as he could plunge into his body. This too had happened at least four or five times before, but Smollins had the misfortune of becoming an All-American and the Boston Celtics number-one draft choice. In training camp, when the holes on his arm were connected by the team physician, they spelled out "You got fucked out of a half million and a wasted draft pick" and Red Auerbach freaked out. Charley was fired on less serious (but also true) violations and Smollins left the U.S. to play pro ball in Milan where the dope is cleaner and cheaper and a junkie can average 30 easy points a game. And Charley, too, disappeared down a sewer—but the slime and shit covering his body only meant that Pechman could get a big name for next to nothing.

Charley was an easy-going coach—he never bothered us and we never bothered him. He made sure that the guys who wanted to play got their time and he kept Pechman away from us as much as possible. The ballplayers dug him for another reason—we realized that he was hanging around, picking up on those easy, slippery checks just like we were.

Charley came into the locker room earlier than usual, solely to speak to me. "Bo," he said as he sat down on the stool next to mine, "you'll never get anywhere in this game if you don't have heart. You've just gotta have heart."

His eyes had flashes of something in them, but they were only static electricity and heat lightning. "Sure, coach. I understand. I'll see what I can do."

"Okay," he said as he patted my shoulder, his duty done and his evening's wages earned. Charley then called his congregation of braggarts and whoremongers to order and, standing next to Pechman and son, he delivered his pregame sermonette.

"This is the second game of a best-of-five-game series in which every odd game—and some of them are very odd—is played at home. Tonight is an away game . . . So remember this is a family crowd and don't embarrass yourselves out there . . . That's it."

David glanced curiously at his father, who could only manage a shit-eatin' grin for the occasion. And the Wellington Rifles roared out of the room and on to the court, hoping to lose a respectably close ballgame to the Elizabeth Miners and even the APBA championship series at one game apiece.

The start of the game was delayed for the presentation of the Miners' Most Valuable Player award as determined by the

Elizabeth chapter of the CYO. The presenters were three 10-year-old girls with bland, accepting faces that only a Mother Superior could love. They were crisply attired in blue plaid skirts and black jackets emblazoned with monograms announcing that they were honor students at Our Mother of the Most Sacred Uterus Grade School. The recipient was one Sidney Elijah Cooper. And when he accepted the award—a $15 gift certificate to the local Army-Navy store—TC peered at the kiddies like King Kong eyeballing three Fay Wrays. One of them exploded into tears when "Sidney" patted her little head.

Finally, after the further pageant and spectacle of a Boy Scout Honor Guard—replete with wooden rifles—and an a cappella version of the "Star Spangled Banner" by the Elizabeth High School glee club, the fucken game got started.

Tarzan knew exactly where the game was being played, so he didn't waste his energy pummeling every moving body he saw. The Miners were winning and this seemed to banana him out quite nicely. Every once in a while, however, he made one of his grunto-destructo moves to the basket just to keep the flies off his ass. But otherwise he was a regular Ferdinand the Bull.

As predicted, Lacey went into heat and started hoisting up everything but the reserved seats. Whenever he made a couple in a row, Foot slowed him down by bouncing a pass off Lacey's head and into the stands. At one point we were only down by 3, so Foot clamped onto a rebound, blithely dribbled down the length of the court and missed a 5-foot jump shot by six feet. After he had done this four times in a row, Lacey got the clue and started committing palming and walking violations whenever he deemed it necessary.

While all of this was going on, Will picked up three immediate charging fouls trying to take Brennan to the hoop. Will's solution was to stop driving and start taking 30-foot wish shots—a tactic which seemed to please everybody.

When we sauntered into the dressing room at the half, I hadn't played and we were down 71 to 62.

Most the gibble-gabble in the locker room concerned the young lady Lavern Mathews had been foolish enough to bring to the game. Lavern is a 6-5, 175-pound forward who is universally hailed as being the ugliest black man alive. When Lester Maddox talks about the social, economic and educational progress the blacks have made since the Civil War, you know he's really thinking of somebody like Lavern. Mathews' forehead, for example, extends over his eyes like a sloping awning—his nose is spread from cheekbone to cheekbone like a flat piece of lumpy tar, but his most hideously prominent features are his lips. They are shapeless, flapping pieces of cartilage which hang like an old lady's tits, and which have not yet mastered the art of coherent speech. As usual, Foothead wrote the majority opinion: "That nigger's gran'pap mus' have been a extree good cotton picka seein' as how they let him live and breed and all." And since Lavern was a Holy Roller who was always mumbling about Judgment Day and the fiery destruction that was just around the corner, Foothead decided to call him "Apocalypse."

Answay, Lips' chick was fairly good looking but her fortune was definitely not in her face—she had a huge pair of tits that began their take-off from her armpits and didn't stop until they approached the speed of light. And they were driving Will crazy.

"Lavern," he said, "I got to nibble on those big things. Why don't you introduce me after the game."

"Feck yis," Lips mumped.

Will nodded slyly and immediately went into a heavy conference with Lacey while Lips bugged his eyes trying to hear what they were saying. "You niggiz gaan ta hell," he finally screamed in frustration when Charley unlocked the door and led us back out onto the court.

A couple of significant things happened during the third quarter. First of all, Lacey threw the best pass I have ever seen. He was near the mid-court line and Will was streaking hard for the basket—Lacey placed the ball just out of Will's reach so that Will was able to jump for the pass and do a one-and-a-half-gainer into the middle of Lips' lady's chest. It took him at least 30 seconds of biting, pinching, whispering and slobbering to regain his balance. And a good time was had by everybody except Lips.

With four minutes left, Foot picked up his fifth foul, a clumsy charging violation which could have been deliberate. And Charley gave me an encouraging look, tapped the left side of his rib cage, and sent me into the game. TC let loose a hearty honk when he saw me, but the Miners were out of the woods by then and his grimace seemed to be a little soft around the edges. I felt no fears or expectations of an impending confrontation—the next move would be up to me and I knew I wasn't ready for anything but a quiet castling behind the safety of a row of pawns.

Tarzan grabbed a few rebounds and hit a jumper from the top of the key while I was in there. He presented his body to me in the unlikely event that I wanted to get my shot in, but I just waltzed away with an intense look on my face—"going without the ball" is what Red Holzman would have called it.

I hit on two of three medium-range jumpers and two free

throws when Cody Wells delicately climbed my back going for an offensive rebound. While we were setting up on the foul line, Cody came over and apologized for hitting me. It was obvious that he didn't want to interfere in one of Tarzan's little "situations." That was the first indication I latched onto that anybody but Foot was wise to what was going on.

After three quarters the Miners were ahead 120 to 101.

Foot started the last quarter, but not before giving me a "Don't get too comfortable" blink. That didn't really bother me because the game was rapidly deteriorating and all the players wanted to save something for the fun part of the evening. Every so often the crowd would wake everybody up by hollering "Dee-fense! Dee-fense!" just like they see the Knick fans do at Madison Square Garden on TV. The fact that no one still breathing could ever recall an APBA team scoring less than 130 points in a ballgame did not deter them at all.

The Elizabeth crowd was a more affluent group than the farmers and coal miners who came to see us play in Wellington. Pechman could have sold a whole lot more bell-bottom pants and knitted vests here. Most of the region's coal refining and by-products manufacturing was done in Elizabeth, so the natives were more concerned with the rings around their collars than the rings around their lungs.

The assemblage was primarily composed of family groups of four who could have been auditioning for the Elizabeth Penny Players' production of *Father Knows Best*. Mom was daintily bored with a game she really couldn't comprehend, but outwardly enthusiastic with the spirit of togetherness. The spinach souflée recipe in the evening newspaper was the highlight of her day. Dad interrupted the continual play-by-play conducted for the benefit of his wife—"Did you see that, dear? Wasn't that a good shot?"—with sidelong glances at the forbidden black breasts under the Rifles' basket. Sis was busily preening herself in the hope that one of the players would notice her brand new training bra. And Junior was worrying about how to avoid letting Betty Carlson find out during tomorrow's church social that she aroused him to a perpetual hard-on.

But the Elizabeth fans were sophisticated enough to realize that Church morality belonged either to Sunday mornings or to the people who worked in mines and lived in caves—so an occasional drunk could bellow an indignant "Nigger!" with impunity. This would result in a "Tsk ... tsk!" for the kids to see, and an exchange of giggles between consenting adults. There was also some anti-Semitic stuff, but Pechman and Rudson were the only Semites in the joint so I never let it hang onto me for much longer than the blush it caused. This type of insult never got too complicated because Dad's accountant had enough on him to put him on a chain gang, and Rudson, the Miners' owner, was also the Vice-President in charge of mortgages in the town's only commercial bank.

My sociological reveries were snipped when Foot committed his sixth and final personal foul with five minutes left in the game.

Ambiguity and partial resolution ... apparent crises that turn out to be mosquito bites ... climaxes that splash drily against the rocks and are sold to the rag man the next day ... a game winning jump shot at the buzzer that circles the rim forever, the game ending only when the janitor shuts out the lights.

The arena was cleared of superfluous bodies and the leeches, dung powders and lancets were activated and readied. Charley led the crowd in a homogenized chorus of

"You've Got to Have Heart," while Rudson tried to pass the hat around . . .

Which is to say that, after four and one-half more minutes of farting around, I went one-on-one with TC . . .

Again, it appeared to be deliberate—Clarence passed me the ball in the corner and ran to join the triple pick for nobody that was being set near the opposite sideline. Taking a jump shot would have been avoiding the inevitable—I was expected to go after Tarzan like a bulldog after a postman. And why not? What the fuck . . . ?

I took three hard dribbles on a straight line to the right, and then stopped short and raised my eyebrows to fake a jumper. Tarzan couldn't stop in time, so he threw his body wildly in the air, hoping to block the shot or crush my bones—not necessarily in that order. But instead of going straight up with the shot, I ducked under TC's shadow and released the ball underhanded. The ball banked in just as TC caught me in the right kidney with his hip. I managed to keep my balance and I didn't rub my side until the game was over and I was sequestered in the privacy of the shower.

Charley was smiling as he handed me the warm-up jacket I had left on the bench. "That's the way to show him, kid."

Even Pechman scurried over with his teeth flashing with delight. "I always knew you had it in you, Bo. That's the way to stick him." And he handed me a five-dollar bill.

I realize that people are totally turned on by other people's pain. And if you can call it a "sport," you can cash in on the public's blood sadism and vicarious masochism. I know all that . . . but, even so, what Pechman tried to do was cheap and disgusting.

So I just nodded politely and made believe I didn't see the money—I wasn't going to accept a reward for being sucessfully baited into exposing my one and only body to some unnecessary brutality. And five bucks is certainly not boon enough for a week's worth of pissing blood.

The whole thing was ridiculous. There had been no checkmate intended—there was merely a black rook maliciously caving in on a white pawn who was trying to find an innocent angle on an empty-looking red square.

I stayed in the shower until the room was empty—I didn't want to read the glimmer in Foothead's eyes. After a while, Cody Wells came in looking for Lavern Mathews, and seeing me alone and in obvious distress, he asked if I needed a lift to Wellington.

RIFLES	FG	FT	P	MINERS	FG	FT	P
Jones	8	0-4	16	Simonds	19	14-17	52
Freeman	15	2-2	32	Brennan	10	9-10	29
McLean	5	2-2	12	Cooper	10	5-8	25
King	4	0-1	8	Wells	6	10-15	22
Williams	17	6-6	40	Middleton	5	6-9	16
Fitzgerald	2	0-0	4	Johnson	4	2-2	10
Lassner	3	1-1	7	Hamilton		DNP*	
Paterson	4	0-0	8	Daniels	4	1-2	9
Wilson	2	0-2	4				
Mathews	4	1-1	9				

RIFLES	30	32	39	39 — 140
MINERS	40	31	49	43 — 163

* DNP - Did Not Play

74

CHAPTER SIX

COAL MINERS HAVE NO USE FOR MAIDS, chauffeurs, sixty-year-old cleaning "girls," or people who will work cheaper than they will, so I expected that most of the black partying would be done in Elizabeth that night. I was therefore surprised to discover that Cody Wells was on his way to a lively gathering back in Wellington.

"The dope man is back in town," he explained.

During the two-hour drive, Cody said several things which also snuck up behind me and tapped me on the shoulder. We started off by exchanging the most general comments on the game, right off the top of our heads . . . and his tone was loose and comfortable. But as soon as I started scratching at Lacey and Will, I noticed a change. Cody had played high-school ball under a "back-to-basics" coach who later had a shot with a pro team. But NBA ballplayers on franchises with a chronic history of losing do not want to be taught how to play basketball properly . . . and Cody's ex-coach had been fired after half a season. Wells himself had a frail, hollow-chested body, but his head was a compendium of all kinds of basketball savvy. He had been a twelfth-round NBA draft choice several years ago, but once camp started his body had broken down in a hurry and he hadn't survived the first cut. And he seemed to be very defensive about the APBA's playground style of ball.

After telescoping his eyes back into the shadows of his head to try and find the lens that could focus on me best, he began to .

lecture me calmly and very patiently . . . I was a shooter, so some minimal degree of respect was in order.

"Don't let those buzzards fool you," Cody said. "They show you what they want to see, and their eyes are always wide open."

"I know that," I said. "But I still can't understand their game. I mean, I see it and maybe I can understand where it came from, but they're not junior-high-school kids anymore. You'd think they'd have learned something about playing basketball by now. It's just so stupid . . . they have to work so hard for whatever they get."

"It's called the 'soul' game, man, and when you grow up in Bed-Stuy or Harlem . . . that's one of the somethings you have to learn.

"Listen to me . . . you live with rats and cockroaches and junkies trying to swipe at your milk money on your way to grammar school. Your head is pieced together in the street, where everybody is looking for the same thing—an extra edge. Where you've got to jive to survive. And you see the pimps and the coke dealers driving the fancy shorts and the fancy mamas, and it all looks so good—and you want a piece of it. But your cousin and ten other cats you know have all done 'nigger time' in the joint, and you're only a kid but you can dig on how fucked up and mean they are. And there ain't any black doctors or lawyers or CPA's in Brownsville, right? Then you see Clyde Frazier on TV, dancing and prancing and looking fine—you see him selling this and selling that, and cruising the streets in a purple Rolls Royce . . . a purple one, right? And by this time you realize that you've got to do it all by yourself, that the only time anybody takes your hand is to try and slip off your ring. So you play basketball. You can become a man . . . you can define yourself without killing and stealing and winding up like your cousin. And all that bullshit they push at you in school about how many bananas South America exports, and how Uncle George Washington Carver invented the peanut . . . none of that does a thing for you. It doesn't kill any rats, or fill your belly, or take your sister off the streets, or even keep that big dude from down the block off your jump shot. So instead of reading about a dead cat named Shakespeare, instead of beating a cat over his head and making off with his wallet, you pick his pants by faking, juking and making him look like a chump . . . and it really does you good . . . it feels real good. Then you go to high school or college and some white coach, like Charley Butler used to be, tells you that you don't mean nothing . . . it's the team that counts. That you've got to depend on the other four guys if you're going to make it. Everybody has to help each other, right? Now let me ask you . . . how can a black kid from Bed-Stuy believe all that? So now you're 'copping an attitude' and you don't get to play and you die, man . . . you bleed and die. It's like being in the Marines . . . they break you down to nothing and then build you up again 'right' way. And you bend your head and do it because you have to live and that's the only way you know how . . . and what's one more rip-off? And then you get a chance to play in a league like this . . . and it's like being let out of jail."

He gave me a flicker as he changed lanes to tell me that I was a virtual innocent and that it wasn't really my fault—but for some reason all I could think of was what might have happened if Pechman had handed me ten dollars.

None of what Cody said was a total revelation, I had seen the practice and some of the theory at JHS 98, but he did seem to crystalize a few things and make them live—and he didn't alienate me with any jive metaphors. But I was afraid to grab on to the whole package—I knew what a sucker I was for "sincerity." And I also knew how much I wanted to believe in people.

After a quiet minute, I said, "What you say makes sense, but I don't know ... maybe it's easier to understand something intellectually than emotionally ..."

"Okay, man, you go on and do what you have to do," Cody said. This time his eyes were smiling too.

The Jermyn Hotel always made me think of what the official Rockefeller family mausoleum should look like—75 rooms with hot and cold running formaldehyde. All of the furniture in the lobby looked like it was made of burlap-covered stone and even though the place was immaculate, as soon as I walked through the revolving door my nostrils became distended with the stale smell of accumulated dust. And if I turned my head quickly enough, I could catch one of the arthritic bellhops ducking behind one of the several marble posts that kept the ceiling off the floor. I've had a front-row seat for their vaudeville act many times—when a guest checked in and managed to corner one of them, a ridiculous old man dressed in a "Call for Philip Morris" uniform would cough, wheeze and fart as he strained over the luggage. The guest would invariably feel guilty, pick up his suitcase, follow the bell-limp to his room, and lay out an overly generous tip to get the Angel of Death away from him as quickly as possible.

Even though it was the only hotel in Wellington, the Jermyn was always deserted—in spite of this, it was one of the city's most successful businesses. The owner, Walter Jermyn, was a home-grown real-estate operator who had installed a private elevator which made only two stops—a secluded section of the basement garage and the top floor. It was in constant use from Monday through Friday, especially during the hours of 12 to 3 and occasionally after 5. The employees called it the "Secretary Special." The goings and comings of the customers were carefully plotted so that none of them ever saw any hotel personnel except for the non-English-speaking Chinaman who parked the cars. The hotel's fee, in cash of course, was left in an envelope on a dresser, and Jermyn himself was the only one who saw the money and made the necessary arrangements. The system had one flaw—Lacey Freeman. He had taken the Chinaman under his wing, loaded him with opium, provided a photograph of Arnold Pechman, and worked out a calligraphic system for writing dates and times. "Just in case," was Lacey's rationale. Now if he could only learn to use a pick . . .

The Jermyn also had a monstrous old-fashioned ballroom and banquet hall with parquet floors and floor-to-ceiling french doors leading out to a geometrically laid-out parking lot. Unfortunately, the Old Testament Social Club's annual bacchanalia were the only formal events which were regularly held there. The local chapter of the Mine Worker's Union wanted to have its Christmas Party in the room, but Jermyn refused—he didn't want his respectable hotel turning into a hangout for Communists. Twice a month, however, every revolutionary in Wellington could pay $2.50 at the door and gain admittance into a public dance—based, said the sign, on some kind of "exotic" theme. Tonight, a gum-chewing, me-zuzah-brandishing chick was being billed as Bellina the Belly Dancer.

My room, at a reduced rate of two bucks a night, was right over the ballroom's stage. I would have the pleasure of hearing Bellina try to coax a bevy of drunken coal miners into doing a bump and grind. The room came with a kitchen chair, a bureau, and a bed with a gigantic marshmallowian mattress. There was also a bare set of radiator pipes which would begin to clang just before the rising of the sun, and the bathroom was down the hall and to the left. Pissing in the sink saved a lot of time and trouble, and it freshened up the air. Ziva Zahavy would have given the Jermyn Hotel five stars.

As soon as I checked in and walked up the back stairs to my room, I dropped my clothing and spent several minutes watching my right side turn purple. It was going to be quite an esthetic bruise—already there was a blotch of orange near the point of the hip bone. It looked like a surrealistic tattoo of the moon exploding. But my urine was only a shade or two darker —TC must really be slowing down.

I was sitting on the edge of the bed, poking and stroking my side and otherwise getting acquainted with some new lumps and scratches—when somebody knocked on the door. It turned out to be a teenage chick who had long, straight blond hair, and a thinnish body that was budding into a peachlike firmness. She could have been a joyous, frolicking cheerleader except that her otherwise innocent features were sharpened with contempt and ambition. She was holding a Wellington Rifles' program—I could see David's neon face on the cover.

"Are you Robert 'Bo' Lassner . . . number 41?"

"Yes."

"How about a quick fuck?"

A few rolls, a tussle and a half—and then the buzzer sounded. The whole thing was about as satisfying as sucking on a sour tooth. And before she had rezipped her jeans, she asked me if I knew which room Eddie Paterson—"number 34"—was in. I guess she was starting with the scrubs and was working her way up to the likes of Lacey and Will. I should have asked her if I had been first on her list . . .

It all reminded me of the first time I got laid. I was a 17-year-old sophomore, and we were in the middle of our only overnight trip of the season—to Danbury, Connecticut. On the bus ride, a cheerleader named Rochelle ("Call me Shelley") Goldberg declared that the proper way to celebrate Hunter College's first plunge into the big time was to take on the entire varsity basketball team. This blessing also brought with it some tricky problems—the freshman team, for example, was in an uproar. Their cries of "classism" and "aristocratic brutality" were somewhat allayed when it was pointed out that Rochelle (we never called her Shelley) was only a junior and would be back next year. Rochelle would, therefore, provide an added incentive for making the varsity—and vice versa.

The remaining problem required much more serious adjudication—there were 12 of us on the team and nobody wanted to be the last man down the chute. After rejecting alphabetical order and physical size as acts of God, we decided that the fucking order would be determined by the individual point totals accumulated against the very weak Danbury State team. Rebound totals would be used in case of any ties . . . and so on down to seven decimal places.

I couldn't have been happier with the arrangements—Hunter averaged around 60 points a game and I was to blame for at least a third of them. Our offense consisted of four guys standing still and watching me roll from one side of the foul lane to the other—and waiting until I had a good-enough position to be passed the ball. Orders from the coach, in fact, were that no one could take any shot except a lay-up without first checking to see if I possibly had a better one.

It's a shame that my basketball ability really didn't warrant such Mikanesque attention. It seems that Hunter's coach, Pete Kurtz, was dreaming of succeeding John Wooden. Given a powerhouse team, the UCLA athletic director would come running to Jerome Avenue in the Bronx with a bag of money once Wooden retired. It's unfortunate that the Hunter Hawks were really a bunch of turkeys. We were 9 and 10 in my sophomore year, then we were 10 and 9 before we peaked during my senior year—12 wins and 9 losses. But Kurtz wouldn't let a thing like lack of ability shrink his ambitions—he realized that, besides having a winning team, a coach's best friend was an All-American player. And if you can't find one, you make one by creating a situation where somebody on your team scores a lot of points. So because I took all the shots, because I was staying in the game whenever we were either ahead by 20 or behind by 20, and because I was being protected from fouling out and losing playing time by hiding behind an especially designed zone defense, I finally got laid.

But it was close. Danbury State was totally helpless—they proved to be the only team on our schedule that we were able to run on. So while our guards were fluttering up and down the court shooting uncontested lay-ups, I had visions of Rochelle's pearly gates being covered with cold "gwax" by the time my number was called. We were up by 20 at the half and I only had 6 points—so, naturally, I began to pout. Kurtz was in a panic lest we blow his $50,000-a-year job at UCLA, so he forced us back into our regular offense. Everybody screamed their heads off, but I wound up taking the first free throw at Rochelle's hoop.

Growing up in the Bronx and playing basketball, football, baseball, punchball, stoopball, stickball, handball, boxball, etc.—a fellow was ostracized if he was caught talking to someone without balls. And who would dare to play doctor or you-show-me-yours-and-I'll-show-you-mine at the cost of not getting chosen into an important game?

So Rochelle was the first. It was not quite the Lord Byron meets the Lady of the Lake that I had been expecting, but it beat my right hand on my prick—and vice versa.

There developed one more complication, however. After the starting five had concluded their post-game intra-view, it was discovered that a volcano-pimpled sub named Joel Shapiro had miraculously scored 7 points, putting him sixth on the clit parade. But Shapiro was too much even for Rochelle—she put her foot and her dress down. A vote was commissioned to bypass Joel, but even though it passed 11 to 1, the resulting hullabaloo reduced Rochelle to tears. "I'm not a whore," she kept saying. "Can't a girl just have a good time?" And the show closed in Connecticut, never to be revived—Rochelle flunked out of school two weeks later.

After little Miss Jiffy Fuck left, I peeked out the door to see how Eddie would handle the situation. Paterson was a grave, hard-working 35-year-old swingman who had been a high school All-Universe in New York City many years ago. He had attended Duquesne for a while, averaging 40 points a game on the best freshman team in the country and watching the pro scouts already jockey for position—and then Paterson got involved with Dickie Morales. Morales was an ex-NBA star who got bounced out of the league for supposedly betting on "his own team"—a public judgment much like the marginal recruiting violations which accrued around the neck of Charley Butler. The truth was that Morales was shaving points and the NBA thought it vital to keep itself unquestionably virginal in the wake of the periodic gambling scandals which socked college basketball. If the purity of the pro game was ever left publicly unwiped, the bettors would rather spend their money on Savings Bonds. And NBA ballgames in big gambling towns like New York, Detroit and Chicago would quickly degenerate into "exhibitions"—like professional wrestling and the roller derby. Then the league would have to court the hayseed block in order to survive. The American Basketball Association, subsequently, will never create enough fan interest until the average pinhead in the street can get a line on every regular season and playoff game.

So Morales pleaded guilty to lesser charges—and the whole world was a happier place. No one wound up in jail and the NBA point spread was kept inviolate.

But while Caesar's sheets may have been properly dry-cleaned, the working boola-boola ballplayer's linen was stained with scum and blood—so Morales turned his attentions to the college game. And Paterson, a poor illiterate kid from East New York, followed in well-worn sneaker-steps and sold a few ballgames for some petty cash, a used car and some white pussy. Nothing was ever proved, but Eddie suddenly —and voluntarily—made an exit stage left out of Duquesne after his sophomore year. He resurfaced a few years later in the APBA as one of the glamorous but tainted names which infected every club's roster and which allowed the league to get its fart balloon off the ground.

When Connie Hawkins' famous ghostlike transgressions bowed to the superior morality of a multimillion-dollar law suit and gained a monster contract from the NBA, Paterson quickly consulted a lawyer of his own. But the average unwashed sniffer of unwashed jockstraps had forgotten all about Eddie's razzle-dazzle game and the resulting court action had all but smothered him in a legal crazy quilt of appeals and counterappeals.

Meanwhile Eddie Paterson tried to reconstruct his life . . . He had a position in the Guidance Department in one of New York's special schools for delinquent boys, he attended CCNY four nights a week in pursuit of a Master's Degree in psychology, and he kept his body ready for the coming millennium by going through the motions with the Wellington Rifles on weekends.

Eddie passed the time with dignity and compassion—and with my head in the hallway, I could see that he was also lavishing at least a couple of very compassionate minutes in counseling a wayward groupie with goldy locks and bigger than average tits.

I could never really understand why so many chicks were so hot to bed down with ballplayers. A player's dong is not quite a joystick leading to a safe landing on the jet set's runway—and giving a uniformed cock some temporary shelter from the Sturm und Drang doesn't mean anything but a good time. There's nothing wrong with a chick unfolding all her wares, but she should realize that athletes are pieces of furniture with little red price tags on them—just like their neighborhood tie salesman, butcher, mailman, numbers runner or grocer. Although I'm told that those grocery groupies are supposed to do a number with rippled potato chips that will drive a man wild . . .

All of this serious thinking was dehydrating my brain, so I decided to venture back downstairs for a can of soda from the machine in the lobby. And, besides, a bellhop had caught me ass-in and head-out of my room, so I was forced to make a move. And sitting there, with chunks of his monster body lumping over the sides and edges of a massive stone couch, was Tarzan Cooper.

He beckoned to me. "Hey, my main man, Bo. Come on here."

"How're you doing?" I said as I sat on a "mahogany" coffee table. "You look nice and relaxed."

"Yeah, man. You got to be relaxed."

I got a breath bouquet as he spoke—a sneeze and a properly positioned match would have defoliated half of Western Pennsylvania. And I felt an honest-to-shit pang for the poor bastard.

"We gonna beat you tomorrow night . . . you know that?"

"Well," I said, "you may and you may not. That homecourt tilt is kind of hard to beat."

"That's a fact . . . that certainly a fact . . ." TC's head started to sway from side to side as the alcohol began to tear a few memories loose. I looked around quickly . . . I wasn't ready for a THIS IS YOU LIFE: SIDNEY ELIJAH COOPER. But TC motioned-threatened me to be still.

"I was good, Bo . . . I could 'bound, I could shoot, I could pick a man to the floor, I could play D if I wanted to . . . everythin', man . . . I could do everythin'. You ask around and see if I'm jivin' . . . you go ask Footie . . . he seen me then . . ."

"Yeah, TC. I know. I heard . . ." But he refused to be interrupted.

"It was the Globbies, man . . . they fucked up my game. I didn't know nothin' . . . cherry right out of high school . . . that little Jew . . . Sabbenstein . . ."

"Sapperstein," I said.

"That little Jew opened up his wallet, turned my head and ruined my game. I was 19, man . . . and you know what he gave me?"

"?"

"Six thousand a year . . . on a three-year contract . . . but he bought me a big-ass Caddy, man . . . just like givin' Tonto some fire water . . . givin' a young, dumb as shit, poor nigger a big car—he'll sign anythin'. But it was a good time, man . . . parties . . . and travelin' . . . did I ever tell you about that hash house in Morocco . . .? Man, I couldn't talk or walk for a week . . ."

TC giggled to himself for a few minutes, while I eyed the soda machine and tried like crazy to salivate. I seemed to recollect Lacey telling me that TC had kept him for two hours once, laying old Globetrotter stories on him. At least he wasn't going to talk about the Miner-Rifle games.

"Yeah, man . . . it was a primary gas . . . I never regretted it . . . ol' crazy Lem made sure the little Jew didn't jap me too bad. But it messed my game . . . the ol' Cincy Royals drafted me . . . remember them? Mo Stokes and Arnie Risen and those dudes . . . no . . . you too young . . . but I was a Globbie, man, so I got tooted for palmin', movin' my pivot foot . . . all that stuff everybody else gets away with . . . every time I touched the ball they thought I'd put it under my shirt . . . every time I came near the bench they thought I'd be dumpin' water on somebody . . . They did the same thin' to Walter Dukes . . . ha! . . . but he had the worst B.O. you ever saw . . . nobody wanted to box him out . . . he played five years without gettin' fouled . . . ol' Dukie, man . . . but they ruined him too. You don't remember him neither, huh?"

As I shook my head he took a long gulp from an archetypal

bottle in a paper bag. I shrugged again as he stuck it in front of me.

"Yeah ... you kids dig reefer and coke and stuff ... that LSD ... but the bottle warms you, man ... right down to your heart and soul."

He took another huge swallow—and suddenly I could see a peep of something in his red and straining eyes. Some frightfully nightmared tooth-and-clawed thing. TC's eyes were whirlpools of ripped flesh and blighted skulls ...

"We gonna beat your fucken asses tomorrow ... I'm gonna show everybody this motherfucker got some life left ... there's pro scouts down here ... John Kurland from Virginia ... I seen him ... needs a back-up center for the playoffs ... experience ..."

He inhaled the rest of the bottle ... and then suddenly he focused his madness right at me. "And when I'm done with Footie, it's you and me ... just like last week. They went and tore that fucken gold ring right outa my hand ... and now I'm gonna rip the whole fucken merry-go-round down to the ground. I ain't no fucken monkey, Bo ... and they wouldn't let me be man enough ... so I'm the righteous and holy fist of the Lord of Destruction. And you're the pinkest fucken horse on the whole carousel ..."

"Hey, TC ... c'mon, man ... I got to split, man ... there's this hot little chick who also wants my body ..." I even managed a meager, twitching smile.

And it seemed to work—a studded iron door clanged shut and hid the brain-eater from view. But I could hear him gnawing on the slick, white bones. TC was smiling at me again—but the fang marks on his neck were still oozing blood.

"Hey, Bo," TC laughed, "I was only jivin' you ... you know

I wouldn't hurt you, man. Shit . . . you my main man . . . Hey! Yeah! You got to come to this party, man . . . a dyno party . . . you gotta come . . . chicks and drinks . . . and all the sneeze your nose can hold."

We were welcomed at the door of the Jermyn Hotel's Honeymoon Suite by a black fop in a yellow suit, and a tidal wave of soul music. I found out later that the former was "Jungle James" and that the latter was Kool and the Gang recorded live at the Apollo. James, totally zooted out in a black tie, black shoes and a black handkerchief flaring out of his jacket, was the area's one and only coke supplier—TC introduced him as "a wheeler-dealer dealer." And whenever James' traveling circus captured a cage full of lions and tigers, it always circled its wagons in Wellington. The local gendarmes dimly perceived that "coke" was either a registered trademark, or a solid, carbonaceous fuel obtained by heating coal in ovens to remove its volatile constituents. So the heat was never turned on and Jungle James' volatile constituents were free to obtain whatever fuel their nasal ovens desired.

There were about thirty bodies scattered all over the room—all of them were black except for four hostile chicks who lasered a "This is our gig" at me when they saw me come in. Cody Wells was there too, and he took his hand off some ebony sultana's ass long enough to flash me a raised fist and an indulgent laugh. A fibrous dope-haze frosted the ceiling and in a corner, on the nuptial night-table was a knife, a balance scale, some aluminum foil, and the biggest brick of cocaine I have ever seen.

TC led me over to James' stall and pointed to the white,

chalky bar. "Hey, James!" he bellowed. "Fill up my man's nose with your poison here."

James gave me a very squinty look. "You buyin' . . . or just tastin'?" he asked.

But before I could answer, TC's intra-cranial Godzilla started to claw and rake at the inside of his host's head. "Do him up, motherfucker!" Tarzan screamed.

I dutifully placed a few crumbs on the silver spoon that James handed me. He was clearly relieved that I had freebied such a tiny pinch and he nodded his thanks.

After he had huffed in a dose that would have dissolved a normal man's septum, TC grabbed a stray wench and locked both of them in the bathroom for the rest of the evening. I found an empty corner, sat back against the wall and let the cotton-candy numbness spread itself as far as it could.

People were shuttling in and out of the room, buying spoons, fractions thereof, grams, ounces and just trying to cop a free high. I also heard one of the white chicks refuse a jolt—"I have these nosebleeds . . . and I don't want to take any chances. I have to get these vitamin K shots . . ." Nobody seemed to give a fuck what she was mainlining, but she glanced at me hoping that her lie wasn't too obviously diffused all over her red cheeks. I gave her a stonily indolent look in return, and she immediately turned her back—retracting both her question and her insecurity.

Nothing else seemed to be happening—just some moony smiles and a few couples fumbling with each other, trying to push the right buttons. But I caught something in the corner of my eye—that old devil, peripheral vision—and I snapped my head around quickly. I half expected to see Foothead wearing a twinkle-starred wizard hat, sitting in a lotus knot with his

long legs tied around a hookah filled with the most other-
wordly resins, oils, herbs and spices. But it turned out to be a
young dude swaddled in a Nehru suit and rapping "meaning-
fully" with the scared white chick: "Now, you got to realize
that the *black* man ..." Shades, and even sunglasses, of
Sammy Davis, Junior.

That was about as much as I could handle. I got up and
picked my way right up into my room. In about five minutes
the marshmallow surrounded me and I forced myself to dream
of soft, sweet and sticky things.

I floundered around in bed all Sunday watching the football
games on TV and thinking about what a fine defensive end TC
would have made. The only time I left the room was to take a
shit down the hall—it would have clogged up the sink, and I
love reading the graffiti there. "Fuck niggers" ... "if you want
to be blowed call 631-1979 and ask for Clara" ... "Wops is
just as good as niggers." But my favorite is located on the
inside door of the last booth—"Nietzsche is Pietzche." Somewhere in the intestines of Wellington, there is being digested a
pale, mutant kid with a chest like a birdcage—a kid who
throws a baseball like a girl and who periodically gets sledged
by the tow-brained apprentice miner-eenies who prowl the
sullen streets like packs of starving dogs. If he ever knocked on
my door, I'd advise him to read James Joyce ... and I'd tell
him to move to Paris.

Anyway ... there's one Chinese restaurant in town and the
resident mole people are convinced that the owner-cook-
waiter and his dishwashing wife are the Buddha's top spies.
Take the chili-chop-suey off the menu and the two of them
would probably have to go into the laundry business. But the

cat is a basketball fan, even if it isn't safe enough for him to come to a game—he'll find a street urchin, however, to deliver any food that one of the Miners wants to gobble up in the privacy of his room. And wallowing in egg-foo-yung like a pig in shit was certainly the highlight of my day.

Later, as I was skipping over to the Wellington Junior High School gymnasium, my favorite afternoon snack pulled gently on my coat—she needed a comp for the game. Tickets cost $2 at the door and in every other pro, semi-pro and quasi-pro league the players get at least two complimentary tickets for each game. But Pechman would try to sell used shit to constipated senior citizens—and he charges us a buck apiece for the passes. No one who asks us for them would ever imagine that we have to pay for them, and we can't tell them without making ourselves look like skinflints. So we end up leaving three or four tickets at the door, and Pechman deducts the money from our game salary.

This invariably causes a rush-hour hassle after the game—most of the players climb on Pechman trying to get their dues in cash. Pechman, naturally, would rather avoid writing out checks for tax purposes—according to the IRS, the Wellington Miners have four ballplayers on the payroll and forfeit all of their games before thousands of empty seats. If you can get to Pechman quickly enough, you can sometimes beat him for the price of a comp during the confusion—but it's usually only a temporary victory. It's official league policy for a ballclub to withhold one game's pay to cover any possible fines—as if any coach in the APBA would be lunatic enough to fine a ball-player. The real reason for this particular bit of thievery, however, is that an APBA contract can be terminated in only two ways—at the whim of the owner and upon the arrest of the player. Hardly a season passes without four or five marginal players getting snapped up for forgery, disorderly conduct, drunken driving, possession, sodomy, or carrying an ill-concealed weapon—so the league's bosses can count on that many no-deposit, no-return game checks.

Theoretically, then, if goldilocks is over 18, Pechman will be mailing me a check at the end of the season—minus all my unpaid comps.

The game that evening was a replay of Game One—the total score approached infinity; TC went on another rampage; every time Brennan exhaled, Will took a dive and drew a foul; I played for 6 minutes and we won by 27 points. I managed to avoid any further damage to my internal organs only because TC was in foul trouble from the start and did his sixth in the third quarter, so we were never on the court at the same time.

Near the end of the game, Eddie Paterson actually used one of my super picks—and he did so with admirable technique. Cody was checking him, and Eddie passed the ball to Lips in the corner, faked away from the pick, then came back and brushed past my uniform as he ploughed to the basket—Cody erupted blindside on my elbow, hip and shoulder. Just before I hit him, I gave that magic wiggle that adds about 50 pounds of force to your end of the collision. Cody blammed up against me and slid to the floor like he had melted into oil. Of course Eddie never got the ball—Lips had taken the pass and put up a 15-foot hook shot—but I was on fire to fuck up somebody. Eddie and I spent the rest of the game hunting up potential pickees. We got Cody once more and that white kid Middleton once.

With TC riding the pines, I was the biggest, heaviest player on the floor, and I must confess it felt good to put somebody on his ass—and to do it legal and surgically clean. I felt invulnerable and a white explosion rocketed through my body whenever I made somebody move. And right before the final buzzer, I popped Brennan with a short elbow chop to the chest.

I was smiling as I trotted to the locker room—but TC pulled the string and I came to a skidding stop. He didn't say anything, but the mad priest behind his eyes was blessing me and anointing me with the waters of righteous insanity.

MINERS				RIFLES			
Simonds	17	3-3	37	Jones	7	1-6	15
Brennan	10	0-1	20	Freeman	17	6-7	40
Cooper	7	2-4	16	McLean	5	2-2	12
Wells	13	3-3	29	King	5	1-3	11
Middleton	9	2-2	20	Williams	15	18-23	48
Johnson	7	1-1	15	Fitzgerald	6	0-1	12
Hamilton		DNP		Lassner	4	1-1	9
Daniels	5	2-2	12	Paterson	5	0-0	10
				Wilson	4	2-2	10
				Mathews	4	1-1	9

MINERS	30	41	44	34 —	149
RIFLES	45	37	50	44 —	176

CHAPTER SEVEN

THERE WAS A SNEAK RE-VIEW playing at the Loew's Lassner, so I lazed in bed all day Monday watching it on the ceiling. It was a one-reel featurette entitled *Bo Goes to a Freak Show*. Whenever my spiritual equilibrium started to list, I would run a private screening to plug the cork back in again.

The film was shot when I was 15—my father had been dead for two years and I decided that it was about time for me to implant my own flag in my own head. (I had designed it myself: it depicted a series of electrons encircling a basketball. In the middle of the basketball was a smokey question mark. The banner I had been flying up till then featured a bleeding hammer and sickle with the words "Oiy vay!" in a cartoon balloon immediately above it.) So I rented a mildewed basement room in Coney Island for the summer, borrowing the $150 from my mother. And I found a job in a fruit and vegetable store a few blocks away.

I worked 12 hours a day for two weeks before getting fired. There were a couple of nice scenes of me snoozing inside a huge refrigerator, waking up every so often to eat a nectarine or a peach. But the 180 bucks I earned lasted the entire summer.

I also happened onto a pair of twins named Phil and Charles who were living with their parents in a bungalow colony located across the street from a municipal parking lot. It was called "The Court of the Silver Sands." The activities there included concurrent, and perpetual, games of mah-jongg, canasta and gin rummy. There was also a bridge game for the intellectuals. The twins' parents were working-class people who had only recently "discovered" the *New York Post* and were now laboring to cultivate a taste for the esthetic things in life—reading Saul Bellow, going to the opera, the ballet and off-Broadway shows. Goldy and Dave . . . they were nice folks and they made me feel that I was important.

Both Phil and Charles were naturally going to be engineers—and three times a week they would take the iron lung into Manhattan for a summer-school course in metallurgy at CCNY. While they were learning their chemical rituals I used to find an empty schoolyard and practice my shooting—or else I'd just wander around the veins, arteries and lymph nodes of Coney Island, looking for whatever it was that I would find.

The first scene opened with yours truly standing in front of a freak show on Surf Avenue. There was a large billboard above the entrance displaying several drawings of the featured exhibits. There was, for example, a picture of a gorgeous young chick wearing a bikini—she was covered with some kind of spots, and she had long fingernails and two fanglike teeth. The sign identified her as "Sheema, The Leopard Girl." Other attractions were "The World's Tallest Man," "The Tattooed Lady" and "Komar the Great"—an armless man who did "astounding" things with his feet. The billboard also promised a "startling and terrifying surprise."

I paid my dollar and entered a semi-illuminated room with a small stage at one end faced by several rows of institutional folding chairs. There were about 10 people already seated and the "show" was in progress. A neatly lettered sign propped up on an easel told me that the forlorn individual seated on the stage was the resident giant. After I folded myself into a chair—and after I noisily banged my shin on the one in front of me—the giant's stare met my own. He tried to smile—out of a kind of kinship maybe—but the humiliation of where he was crushed his face back into a frozen mask of lump-jawed tragedy. A taped voice was spouting all the important numbers—he was 8 foot 1, weighed 527 pounds and was 31 years of age. His name was never mentioned.

While I was pondering how I would play defense against a guy like that, the tape ran out and the giant stood up. He picked up a cane and limped off behind a curtain. I could see the outline of a pair of steel and rubber braces running from his knees to his shoes.

A kid about my age came out onto the stage, put another sign on the easel and replaced the tape cartridge. As Komar the Great came striding out, a young couple sitting on my right gasped loudly and then started giggling to each other. Komar was a toothless old man who squirmed out of his unbuttoned short-sleeved Hawaiian shirt and automatically displayed his stumps. The tape cued Komar as he manipulated a knife and fork with his feet, drank a glass of water, wrote his name with a pencil and finished up with a flourish by picking his nose with his toes. The young couple laughed.

A new sign announced the impending presence of Sheema —I had, in fact, missed several acts. Sheema turned out to be a fat, sloppy 40-ish woman with superhighway varicose veins and several gigantic purple birthmarks. She came out two beats behind the tape's spiel—chewing gum, wearing bermuda shorts and a red halter—and she was heavily involved in a not-so-muted argument with someone backstage.

Again, following the prompting of the tape machine, Sheema squatted on her immense haunches and began pawing at the audience. And in between theatrical hisses, Sheema was straining to pick the sore one more time. Finally she turned her head sideways and snarled at her unseen antagonist: "You cocksucker! What the fuck you think I am? Treating an artist like a fucken whore! Son of a bitch!"

Sheema rewrapped her blotched wares in a frayed bathrobe and the kid came out again. It seems that for an extra fifty cents we could all get to see the show's mysterious featured performer—The Human Platypus. The only spectators who sprang for it were the squeamish young couple.

But I had seen enough. After bopping around for another half-hour I headed over to Nathan's for a hot dog. And standing on the sidewalk, balancing two hamburgers, some french fries and two orange drinks was the same pair of giggling sightseers.

"Hey," I said to them. "Weren't you just in the freak show?"

"Yeah," the guy said. "You were there too."

"Right . . . but I was wondering . . . I saw you go inside to see the Human Platypus . . . What was it? I mean . . . what did it look like?"

"I don't know," he shrugged. "It was dark in there and something was wriggling around on the floor. It was too dark to see."

THE END

Flap-flap-flap-flap-flap-flap-flap-flap-flap-flap-flap-flap . . .

I always enjoyed seeing that flick again. There was nothing like a little sharp ambiguity to reassure me that all my compass settings were properly attuned to the cosmos. It was cozy and safe to plot a course in the general direction of Limbo and allow the Universal Gulf Stream to cradle my basket of reeds. To know where you are going is to anticipate your arrival

—and to anticipate is to care. All of this, I was convinced, led to disappointment, loss and pseudo-death.

It would have been much easier if I had believed in God. I would have been guided by the divine Hand And A Half instead of being conveyed by the divine Fart—but the only "Grace" I was familiar with sang for the Jefferson Airplane.

When the theater lights were turned back on I called Marty. I was getting itchy to look up Rachael and I figured that if I could finagle Marty into bringing Diane along, I wouldn't have to borrow Gus' 1966 Rambler station wagon. And, more importantly, I wouldn't have to drive. The way I saw it was that the time spent behind a steering wheel was the interest you had to pay for being alive. Even if I did own a car, I could never undertake a drive which consumed more than an hour—the trip down to Wellington, for example, would leave me too wasted to play ball. And the looming prospect of having to drive back again would absolutely shiver my timbers. In room 101, after the rats had taken care of Winston Smith's face, they would move me in—strap me into the driver's seat of a stick-shift car during a rush-hour on the Long Island Expressway. And I would confess to anything.

There is usually only one way to drive a car and live to build up a credit rating ... Realize that your life depends on the whim and mood of three lanes of repressed homicidal insurance salesmen, emasculated accountants and frustrated housewives. Driving, subsequently, necessitates a head-cleaving concentration which can only result in one more maniac on the road. On the other hand, what I usually do is blink myself into a kind of trance—relying on pure instinct and reflex to keep my car and my body in separate, but whole, pieces. Or better yet, I tried to arrange my comings and goings so that somebody else drove, freeing me to assume a foetal position in the back seat. Then all I had to worry about was being clipped by a tailgater.

The part was written for Marty—but I also wanted him and Diane along to serve as buffers between me and Rachael. In a fun foursome I usually got away with sitting quietly and saying things like, "Miniature Golf? Sounds like fun." Girls were alien creatures anyway and I felt many different things when I was forced to go one-on-one with a chick. I was generally in awe of them, but I was convinced that no female was capable of sustaining anything resembling a truthful exchange of souls. I was usually polite and casually deferential, and if the lady in question would be kind enough to permit me to slip my nasty, red cock into her lacey, perfumed cunt I would be most grateful. It was good enough to get me by and get me laid, but I only fell in love with chicks that I'd never spoken to.

But Marty was busy anyway, so I applied cold compresses to my still-buzzing kidney while I waited for Gus to come home. I had borrowed the Gusmobile many times before and whenever I placed my request, Gus would wink broadly and say, "Going out with a little cutie, hunh? Going to get laid, hunh? There's a blanket in the back you can use, but don't get no stains on it—my girls use it for the beach in the summer. You single guys really live the life." Then we would reopen the Zovitowski versus Zovitowski divorce proceedings. "Can't do it, Bo," he would say, his eyeballs floating in tears. "We got to be good Catholics in bad times like this. And my little girls . . . they can't grow up without a father. And Nancy, that's the missus, she needs somebody to talk to . . . she can't talk to

strangers. We'll work things out . . . this is just for the mean-
time." Then I would drive Gus to his club out near Orchard
Beach—one of his "drinking buddies" would cart him home
—and the car was mine for the evening. And every single time
I dropped him off, he would turn to me, force a grin and say,
"Watch those stains now . . . and make sure her ass doesn't hit
the horn. You single guys . . . lucky stiffs."

So . . . it was the worst of all possible circumstances—I
would have to initiate conversation, answer questions, explain
and defend myself and drive all at the same time. Faustus,
naturally, kept asking me why I was placing myself in such
unnecessary jeopardy. Every so often he materialized from his
home dimension and mumbled something about "masochism"
and "suicidal urges"—but I was able to override him. Rachael
had said that she was a "woman," and I wanted to find out
exactly what that meant.

I found the bookstore, parked the car and ambled right on
in—there was no doubt that I would at least be driving her
home. She was perched on a long-legged stool, wrapped up in
one of Henry Miller's dirty books when I rang the little bell
near the cash register. She looked up with annoyance—and I
could see her face making the necessary adjustment to "this"
universe.

"Hi, Rachael. Remember me?" Like a little boy asking for a
bite of her ice-cream cone.

"Sure," she laughed. "The Father Flanagan of wayward
books. You looking for more recruits?"

"No," I said as dramatically as I could. "I'm looking for you.
What time are you finished here?"

She mugged a serious face. "Sounds very heavy . . . I get out
in ten minutes. Want to get some eats?"

Fifteen minutes later we were on our way to Coney Island—"I once spent a summer there," I explained, "and there's a great Italian restaurant on Neptune Avenue." Rachael lived in Brooklyn anyway so the trip didn't call for much of a detour.

"What do you do when you're not working in the bookstore?"

"What do I do with what?" she asked as she lit a cigarette. "What kind of a question is that? If you want to find out where I'm at, ask me who I am . . . or what I am . . . or what I'm doing here."

I was starting to get nervous. "I don't know," I said. "Most people define themselves in terms of their occupations. Listen . . . I'm just trying to make conversation. Don't bust my balls."

She laughed sharply. "And what about you? Are you 'most people'? What do you do?"

"I teach and play basketball." Now I was beginning to get sullen. Who was this chick . . . Foothead's Martian mistress?

"And is that what you are? Are you a teaching basketball player . . . or a basketball-playing teacher? Is that how you define yourself?"

"No," I said with annoyance. "But it does establish a language . . . a common set of circumstances . . ."

"We're both living in what is commonly referred to as the same historical time and place . . . that's all the common ground any two people can have."

"But we're doing different things with our lives," I insisted. "Our frames of reference are different."

"Bullshit . . . we're both alive and breathing . . . that's our only frame of reference. That's the only thing we have to know."

I was totally pissed off. "What the fuck is all this shit about? Just lighten up, you know? I feel like a fucken bug on a fucken slide."

Her eyes exhaled a liquid sigh as though she had just removed a pair of contact lenses that were two sizes too small. And the freckles attacking her nose flushed a dark brown. I had pinned her good, but the lines around her mouth still hadn't surrendered. And I felt guilty as a thief.

She switched on the radio and tried to find something listenable. Gus was only interested in all-news stations, so an AM radio was all he needed. While she was fiddling with the dials, Rachael gave me a strange look. "It's not my car," I lamely explained—and she had the upper hand once again. But she just nodded and settled on a gospel station out of West Virginia. We listened to a couple of minutes of Jesus Screaming before she clicked the set off.

"You said you're a basketball player . . . where do you play? The . . . what's their name . . . Nats . . . Nips?" This time her inquisition had a teasing manner about it.

"The Knicks? No, no . . . I play in a shady minor league in Pennsylvania."

"Oh." She lit another cigarette. "And what about the rest of you? How do you spell your name . . . B-e-a-u . . .?"

"It's Bo . . . as in Little Fucken Bo Peep. What is this . . . Twenty Questions?"

"What kind of a fucken name is that for a guy your size? That's either a faggot movie star or a circus midget."

"It's short for Robert . . . but it's kind of a basketball name . . . Bo Ellis . . . Bo Erias . . ."

"You're really into basketball, hunh? What are you, a junkie?"

103

"Maybe . . . I guess I am."

"What does that mean?" she asked.

"I guess it means that I'm going to have to deal with you pretty fucken soon . . . or something like that."

She laughed again—but it had a soft resonance this time. It wasn't being used for debating points. And the sound of it made me feel good—and it seemed to bring us together a little bit.

We stopped off at Nathan's for some hors d'oeuvres—"Just for old time's sake." But it wasn't quite the same—all of the old Jewish misanthropes whose sweat used to sizzle on the grills were gone. They had been replaced by a collection of arrogant blacks and Puerto Ricans. It ruined it for me—taking food into your body should be a personal thing.

We hurried over to Carlo's—the place had been owned by the Mafia when I had first come across it. It was used as a dropping-off place for numbers runners. Carlo was the retarded brother of some big shot and he and his idiot wife were entrusted with creating a convincing front. Since food was merely a by-product of the establishment, Carlo served it up good and cheap. The mob had eventually moved on to drugs and the numbers operation had been "raided"—but Carlo was given the place as a reward for his services. It was a tiny, spotless storefront with a cheap gondola mural on the wall and on the menu covers. A sign in the window read, "Wi serve denner now."

While we were waiting for our food, Rachael started talking about herself—it came out like a tidal wave. "I don't hang out much," she said. "Most people are so fucken plastic and dead that they make me puke. Their heads are like clenched fists . . . Sometimes working in that fucken place makes me sick. All of that madness just backs me into a corner. And I get wound up too tight. Then I go around like the Voice of Truth, picking at everybody's toenails until I find a trace of clay . . ." She quivered a half smile like a tentative white flag. "And besides that, I'm six foot one."

I gave her an incredulous look. "Big shit. You're a fucken ball-handling guard."

She melted into that same God damn smile I had seen the night of the concert. Son of a bitch! I cleared my throat like Andy Hardy at his first church dance. "What kind of things do you read . . . besides pornography, that is?"

She laughed again. "I read about things like dolphins a lot. There are so many weird things in the universe, but the top of your head has to be lifted off to let it all in. You can't be hung up on rationalism, you know what I mean? Like dolphins, for example. Do you know where they're from?"

Ordinarily, I would have said "Miami" and gloated over her confusion. But I just shook my head.

She licked some tomato sauce off her fingers, wiped her hands on her dungarees and continued. "They're from Atlantis, man. And they're the most intelligent animals on the face of the earth. They raise and train some of them to be stupid—to live in zoos and do tricks in aquariums. This protects the rest of them. It keeps us away, right? 'Cause they know we'd just fuck them up good if we were hip to how smart they really are."

Then she did a flying saucers–astrology–psychic phenomena number for the rest of the evening. And she did get me involved. If anybody presented me with an argument containing the words "plus" and "equal" I would be half convinced of whatever it was that they were trying to prove. But I would still have to check out the daily rushes when I got back home before making a final decision. However, when I went to take a leak in Carlo's bathroom, I didn't even think of inspecting the color of my urine.

On the way home, I deliberately passed by the Freak Show—it still had the same billboard, but there were different illustrations on it. I pointed to it. "I wonder if they need a new tall man."

She laughed and unexpectedly kissed my cheek. "You're no freak. You're a nice guy . . . really. In spite of what you say . . ."

"I didn't say anything," I protested.

"Yeah . . . I know all about it . . . You don't have to be so defensive."

"You're incorrigible," I said. "If I agree with you, then I'm admitting that I'm being defensive. And if I argue with you, then I prove I'm being defensive. Too fucken much."

She lit still another cigarette. "You're cute when your flank has been turned."

When I parked in front of the brownstone where she shared a basement apartment with three of her friends, we looked at each other, at Gus' blanket . . . and then at each other again. Then we laughed and she got out of the car.

"Hey, Rachael," I called after her. "What about your phone number?"

"What is this," she said, "the fucken Dating Game? You know where to find me."

I drove home in a more pronounced trance than usual. My head was seething with a strange mixture of shame, confusion and elation.

CHAPTER EIGHT

MARTY CALLED ONE MINUTE EARLY on Tuesday afternoon to find out if I had gotten laid. When I mumbled some bullshit about a "tragic but meaningful relationship," he proceeded to get theatrically disgusted and he went immediately into his "cunt" routine. To whit: getting into a chick's head and into her pussy are two activities which are only a few pubic hairs apart.

"You're crazy," was his diagnosis. "It sounds to me like she just wants to fuck. Just stick it to her good and she'll do whatever you want."

And when he found out that we hadn't even smoked any dope, he was a-stoned with indignation. "You're a fucken hopeless case," he said. "Turn her on to one jay and you would've had to fight to keep her mouth off . . ."

"Okay, Marty," I said, trying unsuccessfully to moderate my annoyance with weariness. "Let it drop, man. We've been up this alleyway before."

He would usually change direction at about this juncture —Marty was more interested in perpetuating the fiction that he had a "Main Man" than he was in pushing a little to understand why I did certain "strange" things. And I must have been similarly afflicted because I never scalded him enough for him to stop badgering me.

Marty and I used to hang a lot in school—and it was very easy to cruise forever in Maintenance. But once our geogra-

107

phic ambiance became a bit more clumsy and inconvenient, most of our commiserating and useless advice had been transmitted over the telephone. There were still those occasions, however, when the Special Events—Knick games, rock concerts, dope deals, and a rare party—ran so close together that we rubbed against each other more than we should have. When this happened, our otherwise witty, albeit prepackaged, dialogue often got slightly antagonistic.

But, it's much too hard to wait by yourself . . . So, not unlike the Flying Zovitowskis, Marty and I were locked into a holding pattern. But after all . . . we were teammates . . . and we both did fuck the irrespective Sanderstein sisters . . . and the man did have available wheels.

Anyway, Marty had come up with a pair of Knick tickets. He knew some shady writer who did porno books, and who rearranged newspaper clippings into 60,000 word tomes entitled *The REAL Jerry Lucas—An Unauthorized Life Story* and *Winning Basketball—The Indiana Pacers Way*.

But, Dr. Faustus argued, why break a habit? A freebie is even better than not paying at all . . . and Marty would, naturally, drive me from door to door and back to door again.

Marty was annoyingly early, but he had unearthed another tab of mescaline internally combusting amidst the lint, the dust and some other debris in the pocket of an old jacket. At least he recollected that it was mescaline. But we each ate a half anyway.

To those who have played kick-the-can in the streets, stolen brooms from nasty supers to be used as stickball bats, and who knew the difference between a Cheerio and a Duncan yo-yo, the snazzy colossus on 33rd Street is never called anything but the "New Garden." It's a perfectly adequate place to witness a basketball game and the electric trains in the basement do save some scrambling time—but the place just ain't got no soul. It has no distinguishing flavor and absolutely no smell—if it weren't for the pushcarts selling soft pretzels and roasted chestnuts on 8th Avenue, the New Garden could very well have been made of styrofoam and the pieces of cardboard that came back inside the shirts you send to the hand laundry. I'm firmly convinced that somewhere in the duodenum of the building lies a carefully guarded screw—undo it and the whole fucken monstrosity will fold up into a Chinese puzzle box.

The mecca of my childhood—"THE Garden"—on 50th Street was forever stinking of a deliciously organic compound of elephant shit and stale cigar smoke. The seats were too narrow and the playing court had dead spots which could kill a dribble as effectively as if some disappointed bettor had taken a rifle and assassinated the basketball. But the scalpers and the ushers were kindly and everybody knew where to find the most up-to-date point spread. People lived there—the entire structure was like an old, bulky, befarted easy chair that launched a spring right up your asshole if you didn't sit on it correctly.

After the game, the management would round up a platoon of Bowery derelicts to pick up the cigarette and cigar butts, the discarded copies of the *News* and the *Post* and to wipe the spit off the floor. They were paid five bucks plus all they could eat, read, smoke or chew.

There was even a Nedick's outside the main entrance—it's a kind of Nathan's for Christians—where the bums would wait and drink coffee until the crowd had gone. And there were also a number of transient bars nearby where no proof of age was needed, and where you could slurp at a lonely beer for over an hour in almost total darkness.

But the New Garden is a hotel room—it's one of a new breed of painted concrete ladies being palmed off as sports arenas. The concession hot dogs taste like wax, the mustard is watered and the beer is flat. No one shouts "Fuck you, Wilt, ya' big prick!" from the G. O. discount seats in the upper balcony. And every game attracts a crew who would be much more comfortable attending an opening night at the Brooks Atkinson Theatre.

Ray Felix . . . where are you now that we need you? We cry for deliverance and we are sold Tom Riker . . .

Of course we got there early . . . and a little hallucinatory around the edges to boot. Our seats provided a perfect view of the mannequins sashaying up and down the main thoroughfare behind the Knick bench. Occasionally the conveyer belt would stop for a moment and some Slot A would trade pleasantries with a Flap C, but nobody ever looked anybody else in the eye. They were all too busy scanning the VIP seats to take much note of each other's eyeballs and/or platitudes.

It was beginning to look like a bummed-out night. Although Marty was already lost in his fantasia of cunts.

"Look at that old bitch," he said.

He pointed to a well-used 60-ish gargoyle who was smashingly bedecked in slinky black pants and a tight black sweater fronted with the words "Baby Doll" monogrammed in variously colored sequins. Her husband walked two eunuch paces behind her, smoking a sterile cigar and wearing red plaid pants and a brown corduroy jacket which proudly sported elbow patches and a pocket emblem: "The Bob Hope Desert Classic." Whether that referred to the husband or the wife was hard to tell.

Marty winked at the old chicken as she passed our seats, but she didn't see him. And a closer inspection revealed that her petrified smile was quivering in the corners. I immediately felt even worse than I had before. In a mere forty years my glinting, bedazzling smile would be palsied also.

But Marty had other things on his mind. "She's got a couple of good fucks in her yet," he announced. "Her ass is still nice and tight."

It didn't do any good—the eternal hubbie's cheroot had rapidly disintegrated and was reforming itself into the likeness of a scythe. And his Prussian lamb's fleece hat melted into a black hood. No wonder the bitch was shaking!

In search of some antipollutant to clear my fucked-up head, I zeroed in on a couple of paraplegics in wheelchairs parked near the far basket. They looked so calm—so independently stationary and blissfully thankful. But one of them had a draped blanket instead of a pair of legs—and my gloomsday machine pushed out another few liters of black smoke.

I jumped up and headed toward a refreshment stand for a drink—and I was immediately ensconced by a swarming mass of obnoxious Knick fanaticos waving their ever-ready autograph books.

"Who are you?" their leader demanded.

I'd been through this many times before. What I'd usually do is either blush and say "Nobody," or mumble something about being an obscure Knick of ten years ago—Charlie Tyra or Dave Budd. But I was in no head to be bothered.

"C'mon ... you're big enough ... you got to be somebody ..."

The kid was already preparing a condescending expression as he expertly thumbed through several back issues of the NBA Guide. He made it clear that I would be expected to take full responsibility if he couldn't find my picture and I turned out to be worthless.

"Fuck off, scumbag," I said, surprising myself almost as much as I did him. His disappointment quickly turned into a pure, spiteful happiness.

"Aw, fuck," he said. "You ain' nobody. Hey, Frankie, this guy ain' shit. An' you said he was Phil Jackson, you asshole. What the fuck would he be doin' walkin' around so close to the game. I told ya."

And they all mercifully vanished into another dimension.

I always felt like an imposter and an infidel in this most plastic of Gardens. Kids in the main lobby scrabbling for extra tickets looked at me like they knew I already had my chance —like they knew I'd rather be home reading a book.

And mescaline sensitized my antennae to the point where I felt like a woman who is ten months pregnant: every move, every word, every stimulus could bring on something indelible and irrevocable. That's why I usually dug going only to concerts or movies while I was living better with chemistry—a more controlled input doesn't make me so paranoid. But there still are those free-form intermissions between songs to be dealt with . . .

About five minutes before the teams hit the court, I saw something that scattered silver iodide slivers all over my little black cloud. Promenading around in the finest of threads and stepping high like they held the mortgage on the fucken joint were Lacey, Wilfred, TC and another cat I had never seen before.

Their individual presences were not unusual. They could be seen at almost every Knick game—prowling the dressing rooms and players' entrance, wearing their coke-spoons outside their shirts and looking for leftover chicks. They even called each other "Clyde" and "Pearl" when no one but some mange-skinned foxes could hear them. But I had never seen Tarzan hanging with them before.

Of course Lacey spotted me, and I could see them coolly debating whether it would be worth the lost hyena time to come over and bother me. Had I been with a chick they would have dashed across the floor during a time-out . . . I couldn't even imagine how Rachael would react to them. And I resolved never to take her to see a Knick game.

Knowing that my head wouldn't be violated (for a while, at least), I concentrated on watching the Knicks and their opponents, the Cleveland Cavaliers, warm up. I could tell by the ferocity of their dunk shots that the Cavs were trying to bluff and bluster their way through the famous Garden jitters. Even though they are pros, the only time the Cavaliers play to more than a 5,000 house is in New York—and the triannual shock of playing the kamikaze lamb before 20,000 screaming, warped priestlings has to do some very unusual things to a ballplayer's confidence. And to make things worse for them, the only thing at the game that was higher than me was the point spread.

But my musings were interrupted by Marty. "I have something very profound to say," he suddenly announced. "I have discovered the reason why basketball is such a popular sport." He paused dramatically so that History might prepare to record his words.

"Think of the basket as a cunt, and the basketball as a cock. A dunk shot, therefore, represents a forcible rape—something that all fans of both sexes subconsciously want to be involved in. A long jumper is a successful seduction and a whoop-de-doo move, like Monroe and Frazier make, is definitely a stoned-out coke fuck. A hook shot is a two-dollar job . . . a foul

113

shot is fucking your wife . . . The only one I can't figure out is an offensive rebound . . .

He made like The Thinker and he was off in the ozone again. Just for the benefit of the future generations of sports sociologists I said, "Sounds like a sexy game." And I got back into the Knicks' lay-up lines.

While they were loosening up, the Knicks looked very bored. They were taking weird shots and generally yocking it up. Theirs was obviously the proper attitude, and since Marty was still busy, I picked up the *New York Knickerbockers Official Yearbook* that Marty had bought for his little brother. I've always been in the habit of reading newspapers backwards so that the sports section comes first, and I repeated the process with the *Yearbook*. I soon found myself nodding, shaking and praying over a page entitled "Rules and Regulations of Keeping Score." Let us read together:

1. Record all offensive rebounds with a ?
2. Record all baskets with a !!!!
3. Filled-in circles signify a successful free throw.
4. Half-filled circles signify the Manichean dichotomy.
5. Empty circles signify the One.
6. Three rules beats two regulations.
7. Each team gets four team fouls per quarter, but I can get it for you wholesale.
8. It is of transcendant importance that all totals match.

"Marty," I said. "I don't think that stuff was mescaline."

"No . . ." he agreed. "It must be acid cut with something . . . with whale tranquilizer."

"To keep them from making waves," I said. But without at

least a "motherfucker" it hung there like Henny Youngman telling a "Take my wife" joke in the Jewish Alps.

I started to speak again, but Marty was intently involved with decoding offensive rebounds, so I let him be.

The game had begun, but it took me a while to shake myself down to where I could follow what was going on. I tried to trace the development of the Knicks' multiple-pick, perpetual-motion offense, but my brain was still too fuzzy. All I could make out was a flurry of players running along dotted lines. When the lines met at a crossroads, the play resembled a figure-eight jalopy race. But the constant collisions never seemed to bother the players—they were apparently capable of mentally obliterating any physical hazards and of freely launching themselves into the middle of all kinds of tumultuous situations. And they communed with their bodies well enough so that they always landed on their feet.

I watched their control and recklessness with jealous admiration. There was a time when I truly believed that, given a perfect set of circumstances, I could function without embarrassment in the NBA. I had scrimmaged with many pro players during various summers, but I was always deliberately, and conspicuously, out of shape. Any excuse is sufficient shelter in a reality storm.

The half-time buzzer seemed to be connected to my spine and it felt like an electric whip being snapped inside my skull. The sudden awareness of 20,000 mirror-people frightened me—they were now collectively licking, shining and preening themselves in preparation for the evening's final parade down Super Star Lane. Once the game was over, the frenzy of catching the 10:47 to Bedroomsville precluded any serious showstopping.

I turned to Marty, seeking a worn bedrock station where I could settle out a little more and reconstruct my public face —but he was still as glazed out as a Christmas ham. I then tried to focus on my shoes in an attempt to ignore the noise and the press of Saran-Wrap souls that was threatening to sweep me away. I was really scared and I wanted desperately to form a spore until the game resumed again and I could safely redirect my consciousness on the ballgame.

But a hand intruded on me and rudely shook my shoulder. It was Lacey, Will and TC . . . and they had already succeeded in hoodwinking three gorgeous ladies who were tittering to each other off to the side. The spare dude was nowhere in sight.

The hand belonged to Lacey, and he used it to point at Marty.

"Looks like your date had something bad to eat, man . . ." He paused to let the footnoters sharpen their pencils. "Maybe it was you."

And when, amid the taunting laughter, I registered TC's utterly sinister smile, a booster fired in my head and I was back home watching the scene on live theater-TV.

There on the screen was Lacey—his eyeballs popping like kernels of corn on a hot skillet, his face slack and his body hanging as loose as if he had been nailed through the forehead to the top of a ten-foot wall.

"F-f-f-f-feet," he was saying, "d-do yo' stuff."

Then the camera framed the image of Will's face. It was benevolent and accepting, just like the cripples on the sidelines.

"Hey, mister boss," he said. "Y'all wants a shine?"

"Hey, man," said Lacey. "Don't you lay that on him. Everybody knows that slavery is illegal."

And they slapped their knees and doubled over with laughter.

The picture next closed in on TC. He was sitting on a log talking to a fox and swinging a gigantic club.

"If'n I ever sees that muthafucka agin," he said, "I'm gonna knock . . . his . . . head . . . clean . . . off."

The next shot showed three black men standing and staring down at someone who looked a lot like me. "Foothead!" the imposter said. "I assert my constitutional right to speak to Foothead."

After a brief huddle, the shoeshine boy handed my double a piece of paper which he put in his pocket. Then the screen suddenly went blank.

Another buzzer sounded and I was back at the New Garden watching the center-jump which started the second half.

"What's the score?" Marty asked.

"I don't know."

"Who were those guys?"

"Some guys I used to know," I said. "Why? What did they say?"

"I don't remember."

We exchanged weak grins and then I noticed that the message area immediately above the scoreboard was now showing a movie. It was *The Tenth Victim* with Marcello Mastroianni and Ursula Andress—I had seen it many times before. The plot dealt with an ingenious way to satiate the appetites of potential murderers and thereby insure world peace. Those individuals who felt so inclined registered with a worldwide computer as participants in "The Hunt." Two hunters were then randomly paired by the machine, and each one tried to kill the other. Prizes were given after each successful execution and when a person survived ten hunts he was "retired" with honors and awarded enormous sums of money. Contestants often made additional arrangements with commercial concerns to make their kills on television in conjunction with a specific product. This, of course, involved an incredible manipulation of the intended victim.

The scene I was now viewing depicted Ursula seducing the poor, unknowing Marcello in an effort to convince him that it would be to his benefit to do exactly as he was told. Just as Marcello was about to slobber his agreement, something marvelous happened . . . the entire factual planet of earth suddenly exploded!

When the dust and the cardboard fragments had settled, I could see that, in addition to me, the survivors of the blast included Marty, a pock-faced Italian Garden-cop and the message board.

On the board now were two very dim figures which looked suspiciously like humanoid platypuses. One of them seemed to be holding a microphone and he began to talk in an unintelligible language. But much to my surprise, English subtitles appeared at the bottom of the screen.

"Congratulations, Xyggletrop," the announcer was saying. "One more execution well done. Which one is it now . . . your fifth?"

"That's correct," said Xyggletrop. "And I never could have done it without Gapo . . ."

"That's Gapo," interjected the announcer. "That wonderful spray deodorant for underflipper dryness and comfort. Be sure to ask your Fremmelman for it by name . . . G-a-p-o."

Xyggletrop smiled. "You can't shoot straight with a wet flipper."

118

Then the screen went blank and the pocked cop approached me.

"Let's see your stub," he said. "You don't belong in this seat."

"But I'm here for something else," I said. "I want to see The Screw."

"The Screw???"

"Yes."

"Let me see your credentials."

I dutifully showed him my Bronx Public Library card. He nodded and reluctantly unbuttoned his jacket and proceeded to remove his shirt. And there, where his navel should have been, was the head of a large golden screw.

"Unscrew it," I commanded.

"You're the boss," he shrugged. "What a fucken union."

He took a screwdriver from his pants' pocket and gently undid his navel. It came out slowly, making loud screeching noises as he worked on it. When it was almost all the way out, the cop pulled the screw free by hand ... Then, in rapid succession, the message board exploded and the cop's ass fell off.

As Marty carefully drove back home, he stopped for a red light and turned to me with a joyous expression.

"I've got it," he exclaimed. "An offensive rebound means fucking your mother."

CHAPTER Nine

THE TELEPHONE WOKE ME EARLY WEDNESDAY—I had forgotten to pull it out of the wall-jack. My head was still bobbing and weaving when I finally managed to crank open my eyes, and when I sat up I had to grab onto both sides of the bed to make the universe stay in one place.

I couldn't even begin to make sense of all the residual dream images which were rapidly evaporating from the nether wrinkles of my brain. There was a kaleidoscope of watery faces still lurking there—as well as a capacity crowd screaming obscenities in perfect unison, a crazed army of man-eating cunts from the Spider Planet, and a series of slow-motion amoebic explosions and implosions. I tried to concentrate, to freeze them so I could possibly read them. But the phone rang again.

"Hello?" I asked. "Who is it? What do you want?"

But it wouldn't answer with anything but another ring. And, somehow, that convinced me that when the phone was indeed unplugged, the Computer had a battery of tapes ready to play whenever someone called. Who knows how many commitments I had made? Whose throats I had cut? How many proposals of marriage I had accepted? How many galaxies I had ruthlessly destroyed? I resolved on the spot to pull out the phone, go outside and dial my own number the first chance I got.

My caller turned out to be Mrs. Lillian Meyerson, the secretary in charge of recruiting substitute troops for the front lines at Ryder Junior High School. Lillian was a timid old lady who wore her bifocals around her neck on a beaded chain. She had been on the case for over twenty years and she lived in Spring Valley with a retired husband whom she left every weekday morning at 5 AM in order to reach her post by seven. The only other thing that I know about her is that she always keeps an open jar of hard coffee candies on her desk. I hate the things, but every time I had to punch the clock I felt obliged to eat at least one with a flurry of "Thank you's" and an occasional "Oh, how delicious." And I spat them out as soon as I left her office.

I was a little late getting to school—as I marched to the subway, several passersby ordered me back into bed. They certainly wobbled and deflected me, but I maintained enough concentration to reach school with my body intact.

Fucken Marty and his mutated pocket lint!

Being late—or, to employ the official terminology suggested by The Handbook for Pedagogues, "tardy"—was no hassle anyway. The Assistant Principal who assigned the daily subs their schedules was a frenetic, jock-nosed Knick fan. In return for telling him absurd and blatant lies about his heroes' participation in sucking and fucking marathons and in drug freakouts, I was never given a homeroom class. The jerk's name was Howie Eiseman and he usually accosted me with his paunch and his pasty smile as I was evacuating one of Lillian's candies—and Wednesday was no exception.

"Hey, Bo," he said. "I saw you at the game last night . . . on cable TV. Boy, you really had good seats."

"Yeah, you know how it is . . . Klein had some extras . . ."

"Klein . . . ?" His face sparkled with the hope of hearing a choice bit of "inside stuff."

"Sure," I said casually. "Klein Frazier."

"But I thought he was called Clyde . . ."

"Naw," I said with all the arrogance necessary to force him to believe me. "That's just media bullshit. The thing is that he really buys all his fancy threads at S. Klein on the Square. So his friends and intimates always call him Klein."

I responded to his quizzical squint with the most pacific smile I could muster.

"Klein . . ." he repeated as he babbled over into a drooling giggle. The saliva in the corner of his mouth looked like semen. He was looking around for someone to lay all this information on when suddenly he realized that I was still standing there. So he shot out another probe.

"Klein didn't look too good last night." His face cracked into an anxious grin. "It looked like he was stoned out . . . on cocaine or something."

"Yeah," I said with a yawn. "He just got a big load from Australia . . . nothing but the best for ol' Klein . . . I guess it was just better than he thought."

"Australia?"

"Sure, man. It's shipped over as pastel-colored chalk—all the blue ones are coke. Of course he's also snorting carbon tetrachloride . . . it's supposed to be the latest thing."

This final bulletin proved to be too much for Eiseman. He handed me my day's line-up of gym classes and he bounded into his office to make a few bragging phone calls.

It was becoming very clear that I had to get some food into my belly in a hurry or last night's depth-charge would be sending up more bubbles. Fucken Marty! I sent a stray kid out for a six-pack of Twinkies and a quart of chocolate milk and I headed for the boys' gym.

There was a pay phone inside the faculty dressing room, so naturally I tried calling myself. The only response I could get was one of those "Beep-beep-da-boop-beep" tone changes like the Enterprise's switchboard makes when Lieutenant Igura tries to contact Federation Headquarters. I hung up and began to finger my dime from the coin-release slot when I was captivated by a sudden impulse. I reached into my back pocket and came out with a piece of white, glossy paper which had obviously been torn from a page in the Knick yearbook—the upper half of Sweetwater Clifton's head could still be distinguished. And on the slip, pencilled in surprisingly neat and rounded characters, was a telephone number. Which I proceeded to dial.

The receiver was lifted after several rings and a rumbling voice grunted something—it was not an interrogative sound, but more of a statement of existence. There was suspicion there also.

"Hello?"

Another grunt—of impatience this time, with distinct overtones of disgust.

"I'd like to speak to Mr. Jones."

"Mr. Jones." It was merely a restatement of the theme which I had initiated.

"Yes . . . Mr. Constantine Jones . . . If he's around."

This time I heard a gutteral acknowledgment of an understandable and reasonable request being received and registered. And even though the speaker tried to cover the mouthpiece with his hand, I could hear him carrying out my petition. "Hey, Foot . . . there's some asshole here who wants to talk to a Mr. Constantine Jones. But he don't sound like a

123

cop ..." Then some laughter. "You sure got some strange friends."

This was followed by a short intermission of footsteps, some more laughter, the clanging of some machinery and the operator demanding a nickel—all before Foothead picked up the phone.

"Foothead ... it's Bo."

There was still some rowdy carrying-on from the peanut gallery, and Foot shouted away from the receiver: "None of your fucken business, and none of your ass either. Now you suckers get on back to work."

Then he directed his attention to me. "Now, what'cha got, rookie?"

"A badly fucked-up head I do believe."

"Shit ... considrin' that you called me here I coulda guessed that all by m'self."

"Foothead ... I've got to speak to somebody ... This sounds crazy! But everything's beginning to come down hard on top of me ... but nothing seems to be touching me. I don't know ... a lot of things are ... happening ... but none of them seems to get resolved. I'm just ... confused."

"That's a bitch, rookie ... but I ain' your father, an' I got my own personal unconfusin' to keep me busy."

"Foot," I pleaded.

"Now, lissen up, rookie. I don' owe you nothin' and you don' owe me nothin' ... an' let's keep it that way. Shit ... ain' nobody solvin' your problems but yo'self."

"But I'm not even sure what my problems are."

"You better hurry up and find out then. Shit ... I pat this mother on the head a couple times and he come runnin' along like I gave him the key to my front door. Now stop botherin' me ... I got some work to be done. I'll see you on Saturday."

"Foot, you bastard! You can't shake me off like that. I got to talk to you, man . . . Son of a bitch . . . I mean it's not like we never talked to each other at all, right? Just listen to me for a while . . . I'll even come down there . . . not asking any favors . . . just help me talk it out."

I was trembling, but Foothead's answer was calm and forceful. "Ain' nothin' to be said . . . not to me anyhow. Why don' you go someplace and do one of your Jew prayers . . . ?"

"God has nothing to do with it . . . with anything . . . nobody's kind of God."

"Maybe that's why you so fucked in the head . . ."

"You see?" I snapped. "If you got nothing to say, then why do you say so much? Why say anything? Come on, man . . ."

He didn't answer. "Foot?"

"I'm still here."

"I'm asking you please . . . just to listen . . ."

"Shit," he said. "You're sure a fucken pain in my ass. You know that? Pokin' me with your fucken dumb-ass silliness . . . aw, shit!"

Then he gave me his address, cursed me out some more and told me I was wasting my time and he didn't want me wasting any of his. And he cursed me again and hung up.

20-SECOND INJURY:

TIME OUT

CHAPTER TEN

OF COURSE THERE WERE OTHER REASONS why I was so moved with the necessity of confronting Foothead. I was being pressured by some unknown psychic scar-tissue which had a beat like the toothache blues. And another brain-ridge was being rubbed raw by a kind of futility resulting from inefficient motion and by a budding awareness of my own helplessness. It was like trying to play a game of one-on-one on a full stomach . . . I had no trouble shooting from the nether lands, but it was becoming increasingly difficult to maneuver for a lay-up. I was also discovering that by isolating myself from the ballgame, I had likewise sequestered myself from the living. My dealings with Marty were fraudulent, I was incapable of seeing Gus as anything more than an inflated sausage skin, my father was dead, my mother wanted everyone to believe that they were all deliberately killing her, and Lacey and Will were vibrating in some as yet uncharted dimension. That left Rachael, Foothead and, I suppose, TC . . .

But what kind of relief could I possibly expect from them? Could they ream out my clogged ganglia with an aspirin fuck and a lye blow job? Could they tell me how many jumps over the broomstick would be required for the probe to be withdrawn? Could they convince me of the Nirvana of self-annihilation?

"There's a gentleman in the balcony, Doctor. And he wants to know if you are animal, vegetable or

> mineral . . .
> mineral . . .
> mineral . . ."

The only thing I was sure of was the emotional coma I was trapped inside of, but I suspected that Faustus' Sugardaddy would have some answers I'd be able to use. But I must confess that we weren't strangers.

I had met him at least once before . . .

It was at a rock concert I attended at Carnegie Hall while I was but a sophomore at Hunter. The group was the Felix Culpa Boogie Band—and it was the very first time that I ever dropped acid. Hot off the latest chalk steamer in from Sydney . . . a little yellow barrel of sunshine.

The band's lead guitarist and primary vocalist was one Moss Abaddon and he was what Mick Jagger would have been had he spent four years as a rebounding guard for Swedenborg Tech. Moss was graceful, fuzzy and nasty.

Jack "Cannabis" Anubis was the bass player and he entered from the wings wearing sunglasses, tight black pants, asslength blond hair and a purple shirt with a ribbed cape attached around the shoulders from elbow to elbow. The faggot-alchemist who was also the toughest kid on the block.

The rhythm guitarist played with the electric cord twined sinuously around his left leg like a puny, naked tail. His name was Nick Ahriman and he wore a conical wizard's hat inlaid with moon-slivers and silver stars.

The drummer was a timekeeper named Sammy Eblis, who was dressed in a green scaly shirt and who was primarily known for his incredibly beautiful wife.

But the band's catalyst was a skinny, bald, black slicker who was wearing an indeterminate number of years. He was referred to only as Uncle John and he played an electrified fiddle. Uncle John also wore a long-sleeved, light-green cotton shirt which was buttoned right up to his stringy neck. His pants were brown and expensively tailored, and a pair of black boots concealed his cloven hooves.

And Uncle John had perfect pitch . . . the rest of the band tuned their instruments to suit his pointed ear. And whatever the song was, Uncle John turned it into the blues. He held his fiddle high, as if to show exactly how each micronote of his shrill improvisations was fashioned from wire and flesh. His freelancing was fresh and unpredictable, but somehow very familiar too. And Uncle John played with joy, with sadness, with abandon, but always with unmistakable wisdom.

As his arms flailed and the music flooded my entrails, I could see his eyes searching the crowd . . .

for two for a nickel disposable souls,
for $2.98 reversible souls,
for out-of-season overstocked souls,
for manufacturer's reject souls,
and, hopefully, for the priceless soul
        of an accidental saint.

His music was candy music also, and he carefully inspected and sorted all of those who followed him down the tripping, hopping and grinding avenues.

I looked up at the tiered, concentric balconies of Carnegie

Hall and I could see the firelamps of hash pipes and burning roaches glowing fiercer and more volcanic. And the palpitating sinner of a freak next to me had coal eyes and a red beard.

"It's a great set," he said as he handed me a joint. "They're different every single time."

Then Uncle John did a scat chorus, chanting to the initiated in their own blues tongue. And the flames glistened and snapped and threatened to scorch the porches of heaven ... and the black sulphurous fumes congealed, and the acid-pitchfork started to draw blood.

Then Uncle John moved his lips and Moss sang "The Hesitation Blues":

Eagle on the dollar says, "In God we trust,"
You say we want a man, gotta see that dollar first,
Tell me how long do I have to wait?
Can I get you now, Lord must I hesitate?

If whiskey was a river, and I was a duck,
I'd swim to the bottom, and never come up.
Tell me how long do I have to wait?
Can I get you now, Lord must I hesitate?

Rocks in the ocean, fish in the sea,
They all knows, you mean the world to me.
Tell me how long do I have to wait?
Can I get you now, why must I hesitate?

Hesitation socks, hesitation shoes,
Lord knows, I got the hesitation blues.
Tell me how long do I have to wait?
Can I get you now, Lord must I hesitate?

Then Moss laid out a molten, steely jam . . . and then Uncle John's microphone was turned on full . . . and then he said, right into his fiddle,

"Don't you ever miss an open shot, rookie.
'Cause sooner's just as good as later."

Then my head began to wheeze . . . everybody else was jouncing and spasming to the music, so I sat as still as I could and tried to be rational: Perhaps I was the martyr Uncle John was looking for. Or perpaps I was just an economy-sized by-product which burned nicely and gave off a pungent odor. I glanced at my neighbor, Red Beard, and he seemed to be totally ecstatic. As I tentatively rose to my feet, his whirling black eyes arrested mine. And he nodded his encouragement,
"Go on, brother," he shouted. "Go on and do it."
But it's a betrayal, I screamed silently. It's too easy and too impure . . . all it really is,

is death forever and ever.

Just then Uncle John began an extended violin solo and, to my horror, I found myself beating my hands together . . . only my hands were pieces of bleeding meat. Then I felt a slight weight on my shoulder and I heard a piping in my ear.
"Do it," the voice insisted, and it sang in time to the fiddle:

God can't shoot,
God can't play defense,
God can only go to his right,
God never moves without the ball,
God is a dime a dozen.

133

And my body jerked and twitched to the music ... and I entrusted my tenuous soul to the fluttering left hand and the pumping right arm of Uncle John.

But I could still feel the electricity being generated by the beating of my heart ...

and by the boiling of my brain ...
and by the stiffening of my cock ...
and there was a sudden sharp pang that meant
        a short circuit somewhere.

But still it felt good and I was momentarily enraptured by the total abandonment and relief ...

until I realized with a shock
that I was also an alien in Hell.

I was afraid to go see the band again, and I even stopped listening to their albums. So I was not particularly anxious to see Foothead that afternoon, but the rapacious black hole inside my skull had to be sealed ... whatever the cost.

THIRD QUARTER

CHAPTER Eleven

OFF-SEASON SATURDAY AFTERNOONS are definitely the best times for getting stoned. There's always some kind of social grope to attend in the evening, or perhaps a movie to see with Marty, or a slightly willing young lady to be put away. So the sunshine hours usually coast along easily and crisply, but with varying degrees of expectancy.

A full bowl for my head, maybe some Jackson Browne to rejoice in my ears . . . and the tube shining brightly but silently. And tuned to one of the few programs that I watch: "Dick Clark's New American Bandstand." It's the Atlantic Professional Basketball Association of show business.

I sit on the floor and watch the chicks shimmy, coko and bop and try to coax leaky erections from the cameramen. And I hear the red light on top of the machine whispering secrets and promises to every gyrating one of them: "Rev it up, Mama! Do it real good and I'll make you a star!" So their wares are laid out as fetchingly as the show's dress code will allow, and they dance and beckon to millions of armchair Casanovas to come fuck them and fill their coffers with gold. So they shake and squirm with all the rhythmic sensuality they can safely handle—and they fight their boogie-woogie battles for better floor position and more appealing camera angles.

But none of them ever does make it—and the desperate joy and boredom that their faces spell shows that they're hip too. Diddling the Assistant Director to try and get a ten-second solo shot, finding a partner who's not interested in stealing close-ups, "losing" a strategic button on a blouse . . .

> They're all too alive
> not to know
> that they're already dead.

Still . . . they have to try peddling their tits before they are forced to sell their cunts.

The guys are less ambitious. They are just looking to dishonor their partners. Occasionally a relic from the past sneaks past the censor—a leather-jacketed, Billy the Kid refugee from the under side of the tracks, who's looking for a chance to huddle with a black chick and maybe cop a feel. But the puffed flesh, the lascivious jitterbugging, and the heated tongues and eyelids are not meant for them.

And all of the dancers believe that Dick Clark is a 50-year-old faggot who wears a rug. But they smile at him and tell him it's okay for him to rip them off because he's cool and he understands them. And besides . . . it got a good beat and you could dance to it.

So I used to sit in my room in Mrs. Zahavy's basement and stare without blinking, and listening to something soothing, and puff on my dope. And laugh.

Because I knew that there was nothing at the top of the hill but an open grave. And I knew it was hard to dance and keep your balance—if you weren't careful, you could fall in too soon.

When Foothead hung up, I got the same feeling . . . that I was destined to spend the rest of my life watching little gray and white figures dancing on TV. But it would always be

Sunday morning, and there would be nothing to look forward to but watching David Susskind chat with six ladies who have lost over 1000 collective pounds by eating nothing but Emperor Moths for over a month.

And tomorrow-forever
would be spent in the Gapo mines
of Alpha Centauri.

While I was thusly occupied with the noble and ancient acne ritual of feeling sorry for myself, Howie Eiseman stepped into the faculty locker room.

"You okay?" he asked. He was still beaming.

"Sure." I paused to inform him that I was not in a jovial mood. "It's just that the Knicks lost that toughie to the Celtics last Sunday and it's still got me down."

"Yeah," he clucked, "I know what you mean. When they lose a big game . . . or a play-off game, I feel like my wife's just died a horrible and lingering death."

He stopped for a beat.

"Better make that one of my kids . . . When I watch a Knick game, I curse like a sailor so we had to go out and buy another TV so I could watch them in the den."

"With shit piled in one corner . . . and some gnawed bones near a naugahyde couch . . ."

"Nah . . . I'm a pizza-and-beer man myself. And the little woman cleans the place pretty good."

He was now wearing such a friendly smile that he reinforced my growing suspicion that he was a lot crazier than I was.

He was the perfect bureaucrat.

"Your free hour is the first period . . . which begins in five

minutes, right?" A properly accented, whip-wielding and ad-
ministerial "Right?"

I told him it was.

"I'm a little short on subs today . . . and I was wondering if
you would mind covering a class for a few minutes. We had to
call somebody from Brooklyn and it'll take her a while to get
here."

"Sure. Okay. Why not?"

Go ahead and trifle with me, you
stupid,
grinning
fuckface.

"That's just great," he said. "Here's the room number and
stuff . . . and here's the book you'll need and the lesson plan."

He paused at the door and his right eye collapsed in what I
supposed was a wink. And I prepare to snap his spine like it
was a wet towel.

"And give my regards to Klein," he said.

"Klein? Who the fuck is Klein?"

And every capillary in his entire face exploded with stupid-
ity and shame. "But . . . before you said that they called
Frazier . . . that his friends called him . . . Klein . . ."

"No, no," I said with disgust. "You didn't hear me right. It's
Clive."

"Clive?"

"Sure . . . he buys his clothing at Clive's. It's a brand new
men's shop on Tompkins Square in the Village."

"Clive?"

"Of course. And he also loves English food."

He was still saying "Clive?" when he left. And I could tell

he was already worrying about all of the phone calls he was going to have to remake.

Nevertheless ... the boon that Eiseman had asked was indeed a fearful undertaking. Usually I was able to sanctuate myself inside the gymnasium and avoid all the turmoil in the halls—but now I was being forced to bare my face before the multitudes.

The five minutes allowed between classes ("passing time" was the official term) was supervised almost entirely by a crew of spectacled, red-tied and white-shirted monitors. They were all armed with Military Police–style armbands, blank "Misbehavior Forms" and the knowledge that the Service Credit they were accumulating would eventually bring them untold power and riches. The other students, of course, totally ignored them—and any threatened reportings to the Dean of Discipline were immediately matched by threatened asswhippings.

The traffic was also regulated by a white line running down the length of each corridor on every floor. And passing students were required to always travel in the right-hand lane. So if a kid's next class was right across the hall, he was forced to make a detour to the end of the building before he could legally change lanes. Going to another floor practically necessitated a passport. And there were enough Assistant Principals lurking about to ensure at least partial compliance to these rules.

While all of this was going on, the teachers hid in their empty rooms and stared out of the windows. The only times they were ever responsible for attempting to oversee the hallways was when the principal ordered his weekly "Silent Passings."

"Discipline" was the official term.

I was greeted with giggles and gleeful shouts of "It's the Jolly Green Giant" as I eased onto the thoroughfare. A cluster of Puerto Ricans wearing white tee-shirts and colorful vests pointed at me with their chins and yelled, "Chiquito!" And a clutch of steaming black kids, wearing their sneakers and already minus their books, nodded in my direction and murmured sly insults to each other. Occasionally a kid I played ball with would nod politely and ask me if I would be taking over his particular gym class.

And the girls fluttered and twittered and sneaked up behind me for quick comparative measurements.

Despite all the laughter and the exuberant ruckus, there was also an unmistakable dusting of hostility about the hall. As the students passed, they carelessly punched and kicked one another—and I was flooded with the realization that many of them were quite capable of killing each other in the same macho-playful mood.

Class 9^{17} was waiting for me when I arrived. The classes at Ryder J.H.S. were numerically ranked by reading and math scores and there were only two ninth-grade classes with higher exponents than this one.

There were about fifteen students present and most of them were either screaming or throwing things at each other. They hardly noticed me.

All I could remember from the twelve credits of education courses I had taken at Hunter was, "Will everybody please be seated?"

And it did have an effect. A couple of heads turned with curiosity and some thumbs pointed at me, but most of them continued jabbering and assaulting each other.

"Hey!" I shouted. "Sit down before I get the Dean in here."

This was immediately backed by a chorus of "Ahhhh's" and a counterpoint of abuse:

"Hey, man. It's the cavalry."

"It's Kung Fool come to beat on our ass if we don't sit still and fold our hands on our desks."

"Up yours, teach. You sit down."

Then I spotted Bassett, the kid whose playground game I'd been attempting to bleach. He looked at me with encouragement and he shrugged his shoulders.

"Read the book," he suggested.

I glanced at the lesson plan which informed me that the class was an English class and it was up to Act III, Scene 2 and Line 74 of *Julius Caesar*. The instructions were in a neat, curly hand and they described the hour's activity as simply "Reading to the class."

So that's what I did:

> Friends, Romans, countrymen, lend me your ears;
> I have come to bury Caesar, not to praise him.
> The evil that men do lives after them;
> The good is oft interred with their bones.
> So let it be with Caesar. The noble Brutus
> Hath told you Caesar was ambitious.
> If it were so, it was a grievous fault,
> and grievously hath Caesar answered it.
> Here under leave of Brutus and the rest
> (For Brutus is an honorable man;
> So are they all honorable men),
> Come I to speak in Caesar's funeral.
> He was my friend, faithful and just to me;
> But Brutus says he was ambitious,

143

And Brutus is an honorable man.
He hath brought many captives home to Rome,
Whose ransoms did the general coffers fill.
Did this in Caesar seem ambitious?
When that the poor have cried, Caesar hath wept;
Ambition should be made of sterner stuff.
Yet Brutus says he was ambitious;
And Brutus is an honorable man.

I was interrupted at first by another round of curses, but
they were randomly directed "Shits" and "Fucks." And,
incredibly, everybody not only sat down, but most of them
collapsed their arms on their desks and went to sleep.

By the time I got to "If you have tears prepare to shed them
now," only four students were still awake. And as they moist-
ily reached for their bandanas, the new substitute stepped
timidly into the room. I passed her the book as though it was a
baton and she was about to run the anchor leg. And I scurried
back into the gym.

Bassett's class came in later that morning, so I dispensed
with the required warm-up exercises and we got right down to
the game. Bassett is about 6–4, and he must have been weaned
on pretzels, potato chips, Twinkies and Dr. Peppers. But his
calves are wide, flat and coiled like hooded cobras. And he can
shit through the basket and wipe his ass on the rim on his way
down—so we usually have some interesting ballgames.

It's still tough for me to really level when I go against him. I
invariably spend a few minutes setting picks for phantom
cutters and busting my ass to get good position in the pivot.
Then I have to give it all up and go out to stalk the ball—so I
usually have to settle for trying to shoot the kid blind. He
scores his points too, but I manage to contain him enough and

pick up sufficient smart-garbage to keep him happy and to maintain my own reputation.

It just so happened that I was burning up the nets that day. Most of the time, good shooters have their spots on the floor, their totally synchronized patches where ball, fingers and basket are entirely congruous. But maybe once every ten outings, the whole court seems to be covered with all your little secret X's, and whatever you can get away will fall in. You don't have to see the hoop, or follow through, or even know where you are. All that is required of you by the forces that temporarily control your body is that you throw the ball high in the air. Then you silently tremble with the Presence as you watch it descend in a perfect parabola.

And when you do miss a shot on those holy days, there's nothing you can do but bark a "*Sacré bleu!*," look with dismay at your Judas hands, and brace yourself for the rain of lizards and bats that will surely follow.

And the sun doesn't dare move until you get tired and miss two in a row.

And I saw it as an omen.

CHAPTER TWELVE

TAPED ON THE FRONT DOOR of the address Foot had given me
was a sign which informed the world (and the New York City
Fire Department) that there was an Artist in Residence on the
top floor whose talents were available to all comers: "Your
Likeness Fashioned in Durable Clay Sculptures—$5."

But Foothead's mysterious emporium was one flight down a
clanging staircase and behind an iron counter-weighted door
with its own legend, "Hopewell Enterprises," scratched
through the green paint with a nail. It was situated under a
darkly distintegrating building in the West Village—one of
those musty, peeling places that house button factories, card-
board-box assembly sub-sub-contractors, and loft upon loft of
young Puerto Rican chicks making belts and collars on
hand-pedaled sewing machines.

I rapped on the hollow door and waited, and when nobody
answered I pushed it open. And was immediately clouted by
the odor of some kind of decaying vegetable ... cabbage,
maybe ... but with distinct overtones of garlic. There were a
number of slatted wooden boxes piled erratically against all
four walls, and I could see a brownish liquid oozing from them
into a grating located in the middle of the concave floor.

In one dark corner, a reddish cat with a lump instead of a
tail was poking around. It hissed at me and then started
slapping at one of the boxes.

"Don't mind the cat, rookie. Right in here."

Foot was sitting in a tiny office whose doorless entrance had been hidden behind the stacked vegetation. The room contained a glassless window at one end and a glowing base-board heater at the other—so that half of it was unbearably cold and half was unbearably hot. The walls were covered with charts, notices and telephone numbers. And this cubicle opened into another, smaller, room which contained the foulest toilet I've ever seen.

It was not quite the same thing as Billy Batson seeking out Shazam in the Subway Hall of Fame.

Foot was sitting on a swivel chair with his feet propped up on an old roll-top desk. And he was rolling a joint.

He aimed an eye at a small burlap-covered barrel which was perched along the room's temperate equator.

"Sit down and take a pull on this here reefer. And start tellin' me why you so fired up to come down here and be botherin' me."

I noticed for the first time that there was a radio playing gospel music hidden somewhere in the office. And I could still hear the cat scratching about in the outer room.

I studied the joint. "Must we do this?"

"We use nigger rules here," he said. And the playful, spacey wrinkles which usually frolicked around the corners of his mouth were straightened out. They looked hard and nasty.

I puffed on the joint . . . and every cell in my body contorted with an amoebic seizure. I felt like I had been taken apart and then reassembled in a Stone Age marketplace in the bowels of Zambia. It was doubtless the same wacky weed that Foot had produced last week. I sucked in two more clouds of unknowing and handed it back to him.

"What do you make here?" I asked.

"Money!" he spat a jagged bolt of anger. "Lissen, rookie, I ain' got the time . . . What do you want?"

The smoke was now making my head implode with green colors and jungle smells. And it was raining sulphur in flaming ashes. But I could still see myself . . . I was wearing a safari hat and carrying a rifle . . . and talking to a medicine man.

"It's not working, Foot. I can still tell who I am."

He sighed with annoyed dignity and he fingered his necklace of human molars. "Well now, rookie . . . why don' you just up and tell wise ol' Foothead all about it?"

And his lips mouthed a spell as he fiddled with some papyrus rolls on his desk.

"I guess," I said clumsily, ". . . among other things, I'm a basketball player . . ."

He laughed and turned his painted face to me. Then he spoke in a muffled tone which was hard for me to hear: "Now that, rookie, is a matter for opinion. There's a whole diff'rence between playin' and bein' an actual player. If you couldn't shoot, rookie, you'd be an embarrassment."

He killed the roach and flipped it out the window. Then he ducked back over his papers, and he took up his pen.

I tried responding slowly and rationally, but my tongue swelled up and everything came out in a spluttering confusion—like Sylvester the Cat trying to talk his way out of Bascom the Bulldog's back yard. I coughed up some saliva and tried again.

"You're right, but your're also wrong. But let me try and say this the way I want . . . I really do love basketball. Every time one of those Saturday night UCLA games is on from the coast . . . I go wild with gratitude, and I resolve to become a better consumer. And I never miss the NCAA tournament games either . . . I inspect all the players to try and read what kind of pros they'll make. I also try to come up with a team I can get involved with . . . whose type of game I like to watch. But it's hard to really get into it because it's a one-loss elimination tournament. But it does make a difference to me who wins . . . and I never root for UCLA anymore . . ."

But the sound of chuckling and of rhythmically jingling bells interrupted my monologue.

"You sound like those roly-poly fat-ass kids that their fathers take to see Knick games at the New Garden."

"No, no . . . Let me finish." And I shook myself free of his cobweb spell. "That whole scene is just a warm-up for the NBA playoffs . . . and total involvement with the Knicks. From the Ides of March on, I savagely pine for a Knick-Celtic series. So if my head is committed there, then it should be no trouble doing it with my body, right? So it must be a matter of priorities . . . and getting my bones broken for some stupid ritual is low on the list. That's not my idea of what basketball is. I don't need the game to get me out of a ghetto, right? So I want it to be beauty and precision and grace . . . like a magic concert in the Fillmore East . . . It's creation and energy and even a kind of low-grade communion. I want to be able to watch a game without the sound and listen to my music . . . and slide from one stage to the other without any hassle at all. Can you understand that? That's what I think I really have to do."

"Why?"

It was sharpest word I have ever heard;
and like a razor-comb
it shredded my brain.
But a red scab oozed up
and sealed the wounds.

"No reason," I said. "No cause and effect . . . It just seems like the best way to be . . . for me to be."

"Sounds useless to me," Foot said as he plucked another joint from behind my ear.

"It probably is," I said, "but I can't seem to be able to find myself a home court. So at least it's a uselessness of my own choosing."

"Why you tellin' me all this? What do you want me to do for you? Mix you a potion? Stick pins in a TC doll?"

And the residue of mescaline tars, Foothead's charms and snake oil fumes were forming compounds . . . and rubbing each other. And like heat, water and lightning, blasting life into the primeval mud,

it all fissioned an act of Creation.

And the blood flowed and etched colored patterns in the pink surfaces of my brain.

"It just has to be done," I said with a bit of a stagger. "I feel that I want to have some control over the rules of the games I'm forced to play . . . and certainly for the games that I invent. I don't want to become one of those guys who has to play once a week or he starts imagining chest pains and hemorrhoids. One of those lunatics who shows up in a Y in Brooklyn at nine o'clock every Saturday morning to get a 'good run.' I know that playing ball has nothing to do with building character and self-discipline . . . that's no secret any-more. All it seems to do to people is the same thing that living seems to do . . . it zombies everybody out and forces them to hang onto someone else's life. They all have to own a superstar in order to keep their senses twitching. I mean, there're no

great causes left. The military draft is over . . . so there are no
burning libraries, and no more captive deans. It's all back to
beer-and-jock stuff . . . streaking and getting crazy-fucked
drunk and trying to be a cool redneck. We don't seem to need
nuclear physicists anymore. All those people whose ancestors
were curious about other dimensions are already living in
them . . .

    in crystal cities rising up into the universe
    like stalks of diamond wheat.

And everybody calls them 'trouble-makers.' The whole world
belongs to a hereditary union

    a local
    or express
    a Grand
    or a Western
    but Cooper Union is now a mausoleum.

I just can't be a member of the club that's on the floor now.
Either I'll wait for my next, or I just won't play."
    "Rookie . . . I know what club you really talkin' about, and
you already a charter member. I do believe that's skin and
bone that's showin' from out under your shirtsleeve, ain' it?"
    His atomic eyes pulsated at me and forced me to smoke
some more,

    while he accused me,
    and he chiseled his pronouncement on the fiery air:
    "You just afraid."

But his sneer was just a touch too theatrical—and my membranes tightened and held their shapes.

"Maybe I am . . . but I don't see how that explains anything . . . or makes anything better . . . or clearer. If I am, what do you suggest I do about it? I'm no good at wax dolls either."

He shook his head with disbelief, and there was a simultaneous cacophony of log-drums and bone-rattles. "You come all the way down here to aks about what to do when another man beats up on you . . . Ain' that somethin'? Didn' your Daddy teach you nothin' useful? If you got to aks, rookie, then that's all you ever goin' to do is aks."

And then he threw my eyeballs along the green felt floor of the gaming table,

but they still came up blue.

"It seems more complicated than just that. It's not fair if it's just that simple . . . but I guess that's an answer too. And I'm, sure that I know what you want me to do."

"Then go do it and you won' need no more questions." And he turned once more and chanted quietly to his files:

"Zimba, zamba, zoo . . .
Chump-ass motherfucker . . ."

I took another puff . . . and it turned out to be the one that completely severed my mooring. And my self-awareness

sailed into a diagonal fade-out/fade-in . . .
as if someone had tilted the universe.

Which usually meant that Mister Death had phlegmed his bad breath into my face. He must have been hiding out behind a leaky crate of fermenting cabbage.

And I was positive that Foothead had an electric Stradivarius stashed away somewhere.

But I was smiling anyway . . . and I was feeling fine . . . I could see all this because I was not me anymore, and I could look at myself through a quasar peephole.

"Foot . . . let me ask you this . . .Why do you allow TC to fuck with you like he does? How come you don't hit him back? Why do you want me to do something that you won't do yourself?"

He turned to me and laughed, and the sound crackled menacingly through the building . . . and half his tongue flicked one way, and half the other way. And his cat's eyes sparkled and flashed . . .

Just like a playoff game, or a Grateful Dead concert.

"You poor dumb rookie . . . Don' you unnerstan'? Did you ever see a mark or a lump on me? Did you ever see me bleed? Or piss red like you? Every time he touches me he just ties us tighter together. But TC knows this . . . he knows that nobody ain' free, if they ain' got me. That's a poem, rookie."

I looked at him with shock and surprise, but without the horror I had anticipated. "Is it you, or just the smoke?"

He laughed again. "Maybe it's you," he said.

And, once more, he hovered over his balance sheet.

"I'll take some more smoke . . . if you got any."

Without looking at me, but with his creases folding themselves back into their accustomed amusement, he handed me an already lighted third joint. Which I smoked by myself. After a while, I asked him another question: "Foot, do you like poetry?"

"He put his red pencil down. "Sure . . . I even got another one I wrote: Roses are red and violets are blue, Stick it to him before he sticks it to you."

153

"Well I got two for you," I said. "My sixth-grade teacher made us memorize them . . . and I never knew why until now:

> The overthrown he rais'd, and as a Herd
> Of Goats or timorous flock together throng'd
> Drove them before him Thunder-struck, pursu'd
> With terrors and with furies to the bounds
> And Crystal wall of Heav'n, which op'ning wide,
> Roll'd inward, and a spacious Gap disclos'd
> Into the wasteful Deep; the monstrous sight
> Struck them with horror backward, but far worse
> Urg'd them behind; headlong themselves they threw
> Down the verge of Heav'n, Eternal wrath
> Burn'd after them to the bottomless pit.
>   Hell heard th' unsufferable noise, Hell saw
> Heav'n running from Heav'n, and would have fled
> Affrighted; but strict Fate had cast too deep
> Her dark foundations, and too fast had bound.
> Nine days they fell . . ."

"Enough of that," he said with a quiet, but chilling, urgency.

"You know the poem?"

"It's racist, faggot bullshit is what it is. Teach that shit in schools and fuck up people's heads. Let's hear the other one."

And I closed my eyes and recited:

> My mother bore me in the southern wild,
> And I am black, but O! my soul is white;
> White as an angel is the English child,
> But I am black as if bereav'd of light.

154

My mother taught me underneath a tree,
And, sitting down before the heat of day,
She took me on her lap and kissed me,
And pointing to the east, began to say:

"Look on the rising sun,there God does live,
And gives His light, and gives His heat away;
And flowers and trees and beasts and men receive
Comfort in morning, joy in the noonday.

"And we are put on earth a little space,
That we may learn to bear the beams of love;
And these black bodies and this sunburnt face
Is but a cloud, and like a shady grove.

"For when our souls have learn'd the heat to bear,
The cloud will vanish; we shall hear His voice,
Saying: 'Come out from the grove, My love and care,
And round my golden tent like lambs rejoice.'"

Thus did my mother say, and kissed me;
And thus I say to little English boy.
When I from black and he from white cloud free,
And round the tent of God like lambs we joy,

I'll shade him from the heat, till he can bear
To lean in joy upon our Father's knee;
And then I'll stand and stroke his silver hair,
And be like him, and he will then love me.

I opened my eyes and was startled to see a quicksand

pulling softly at Foothead's sneering face. There was the same foundation of black marble I had glimpsed before, but the center of it was now cleft with a familiar winking black eyeball ... But all it did was make me wonder how much money Henny Youngman's parents had spent on violin lessons.

"Poems never do you no good," Foothead whispered softly. "I'm listenin' but there ain' nothin' worth buyin'."

I told him that I didn't know that I was selling.

He smiled again ... and blew a rainbow-colored smoke ring from his nose and a laugh from the back of his throat. "Maybe so ... maybe so ... Maybe not right now ... But let me tell you one thing, rookie ... It's always nice to know you're wanted."

"Mischief,"
I said,
"thou art a
Foot."

He slammed his hand hard against the desk:

"An one more peep
outa little Bo
and this here ugly ol' spider
gonna waste more than your tuffet.

Now get the fuck outa here. I got nothin' more to say to you, an' I got no more time to waste listenin' to more of your bullshit. So go on, get out."

As I rose to my feet, I stared as steadily as I could into the beautiful diamond-pupiled shafts which led down into the remnants of his soul.

"Okay, Foot, but whatever I end up doing I'll be doing for myself and by myself."

He was already nose deep in Accounts Expended, but I knew that he had heard me and was suspending his disbelief.

And I left realizing I had created my own epiphany. My soul had been clicked back two notches and I had watched myself watching the world through the holes in my skull. And the mirrored space between the world and my soul was a mined no-man's-land

> where Oscar Robertson had re-invented
> The Game
> and created all the Pearls
> and all the Clives who followed. . . .
> and who had also transformed the game
> from a game
> into a metaphor.

CHAPTER THIRTEEN

FRIDAY WAS A PLAGUE. I was boiling with anxiety and I couldn't wait for Saturday's game. After a few hours of gaping at the ceiling, striding nervously around the apartment, gobbling down Gus' last jar of pickled pig's feet and trying to stone myself into immobility, I finally gave up and called my mother to invite myself for dinner. The yellow brick-armband road back to the womb never did too much for me, but I needed the service credit and a good meal. And an uncomfortable place where I could be petty, obnoxious, close-mouthed and irritable with total justification.

My poor widowed blue-haired puff of a mother lived in a neighborhood which was almost completely untrammeled by time. The old Jewish crones still made their haggling rounds of the butcher shops, the appetizing stores and the produce markets—shuffling fifteen arthritic blocks to save two cents on a pound of baking apples. And the antique parents of these wrinkled, shopping nightmares still sat on milk boxes in the sun, reading *The Forward* backwards. A few doors down from the bagel factory, where they could also bask in the aboriginal odors of garlic and sesame. And the only time they moved was when one of them died, or when the wind shifted.

There was, however, one concession made to the Atomic Age: the bent old witches pushed their shopping carts instead of pulling them. This was to make certain that no invading tribe of schwarzers could steal up behind them and run off with Max's bottle of borscht or that tiny precious brown bag of freshly ground horseradish.

As I rushed by the playground I waved vaguely to the usual late-afternoon senate of seers and analysts who had convened to hold the day's debate on the sports pages of the *New York Post*—as they leaned against a fence and watched six twelve-year-olds in velour sweatshirts and expensive leather sneakers play an atrocious half-court game. When my passing was noted, the bobbing of their heads informed me that my own game was in the process of being carefully evaluated. And one of them even called to me: "Hey, you fucken scumbag! Get the fuck over here for a quick game of horses!"

But I made believe I couldn't hear him.

My mother and I went through our normal routine: she told me about her new diet, her new boss, and she brought me up to date on the family's gallbladder operations. While I read the paper, watched a James Cagney movie on TV and occasionally exhaled a barbed monosyllable. Whenever my coma lifted and I discovered her waiting expectantly, I asked her about her bridgework . . . or about Cousin Susan's baby . . .

I stayed for about two hours, kissed her at the door, wiped my mouth with a flourish and told her that her meat loaf was too dry.

Then I walked home feeling like shit, closed the door to my room so Gus couldn't complain about his missing pig's feet, and watched old movies until it was safe for me to fall asleep.

FOURTH
QUARTER

CHAPTER Fourteen

My head was a cancer of apprehension while I dressed for the game. My jock kept shrinking and my sneakers felt like they were roller skates. And when I broke a shoelace, I looked to see if the frayed end had been tampered with.

Lips was using the adjacent space and without saying a word he excavated a new pair of laces from his Adidas bag. Then he handed them to me with a shy, ivory-yellow grin. But before I could thank him, Will and Lacey launched an assault.

"Hey, Will . . . did you peep out Lips' new lady?"

"New lady? Man, I thought she was a old stack-ass bitch just excaped from the ugly parlor."

And from the wings I heard myself listening to the laughter as it foamed into a mushroom cloud.

"Lips," Lacey said with an easy hand on his audience's string. "Don't mind us, man. We're only funnin' you. Everybody knows that you a lucky dude for sure . . ."

Lips' eyes glazed with anticipated pain as he waited for the other shoe to drop. And I could hear my heart beating in my ears like huge drops of blood dripping on a bass drum . . .

("You found the onliest bitch in town who
can stand next to you and make you look
like Sidney Pointiay.")

163

. . . and the entire orchestra exploded with heehaws and guf-
faws.

I looked around quickly to see what Foot was doing.

During the drive down to Elizabeth City that afternoon, he
had been strangely quiet. I had flashed him out once while he
was staring at me in the rearview mirror. But he had immediately turned his head.

Now he was nowhere in sight. In the bathroom, no doubt
. . . firing up with Sandy McLean.

But no matter.

Lips sat down on the folding chair next to mine . . . his
clumsy hands trying to rip the talons out of his skull. And I
could see that it was futile . . . The more he tore at himself, the
more I could hear him bleed.

Without bothering to see where the magpies had perched,
or what they were about, I put my arm around Lips' shoulders.

"Fuck them both," I told him.

He folded his hands in his lap, nodded his head and spoke
something I couldn't understand. But his eyes sent out a
probe. So I clapped him merrily on the back and resumed
threading the laces through the small metallic holes.

Then we all heard a knock on the locker-room door . . .
closely followed by two sizzling splashes and one metallic roar
which broke like a bowel wave over the tiny room. Then Foot
and Sandy closed the toilet door behind them and we all
silently awaited the Pechman entourage.

While the blood now dripped a love song along my membranes and through my why-a-ducks.

Pechman charged into the room like a crazed but friendly

beast and immediately began mauling us with his saliva-ed words. "You know, you guys," he said, "if we can win tonight we'll be the champions of the Atlantic Professional Basketball Association. A nice thing, fellows . . . it has a nice ring to it. We've all worked long and hard for this moment . . . all of us. And we'll deserve all the honors and the ri . . . ah . . . and the glory that will come to all of us. I can tell you now that I've taken funds out of my own pocket to buy each of you a small, but meaningful, memento of . . . of the championship of the Atlantic Professional Basketball Association . . . that we're going to win. But remember this, gang . . . when you go out there tonight . . . to play ball. Think of the thousands of loyal and devoted fans in Wellington who have been a constant source and inspiration to us all . . . and who might . . . who just might be deprived of their wished for and prayed for opportunity of seeing their Rifles become champions of the . . . league. To share the joy . . ."

But Lacey had had enough: "Hey Pechman, man . . . hey . . . hey, man. Slow down. I got a question to aks you."

And before Pechman could get the auxiliary pumps going, Lacey was halfway around the clubhouse turn.

"What I would like to know is this . . . I want my money in cash right before the game starts. Because there is been some rumors, you unnerstand, that some of you cats is aimin' to pay us with checks . . . with checks, man! That I got to pay to get cashed. That I might have to dribble on home, you dig? That's my question."

And Pechman's face had a hernia.

"What?" he bellowed. "Are you crazy? You want me to give you cash money before the game is even played? What the fuck do you think I am? Santa fucken Claus? What if you break a leg going through the door and you don't play? What if the building is struck by lightning and the game isn't played?"

(Foot and I were the only ones who cast a wary glance at the firmament. The former scratching his balls as he did so.)

(Or was it the latter . . . ?)

But little David amputated the discussion by bubbling into tears and dashing out of the room. And his father's eyes turned mean: "Lacey! That's the lowest thing I've ever seen a man do . . . make a fucken kid cry like that!"

And he stalked out after his son and heir.

Before anybody had a chance to laugh, Charley Butler cleared his throat and lightly pricked his fingers on the ends of his gray crewcut. "Enough of this bullshit," he said. "This ain't no circus. Don't fucken embarrass yourselves out there. Remember that you're supposed to be professionals."

Then he clapped his hands in perfect unison, pushed open the door and led the Wellington Rifles out onto the court for the fourth game of the final APBA playoff series.

I curled up on the bench, flexing my knees and ankles in an impossible effort to stay loose and alert. But once the game began, my concentration waned—I soon realized that I had witnessed the very same game exactly one week before. I had already seen Rubber Simonds lofting in his marshmallow jumpers; TC mercilessly trying to pound a passive Foothead into jelly; and Brennan drawing blocking fouls on Lacey every time he chose to go to the hoop. The Fates had already braided and cut the cord as they had seen fit . . . we would lose by twenty points to universal acclaims of delight.

But Foothead refused to act out his assigned role. On the

first play of the game he was charged with a foul for obstructing TC's elbows with his frail but obstinate body.

Okay . . . certainly an acceptable variation of one of the play's dominant motifs. But before the first act was completed, Foot had drawn three more fouls and all of them were deliberate, reckless and outrageously spontaneous: A hack in the backcourt (not to be taken as a reflection on the playwright), a theatrically extended leg as Brennan followed the dotted line to the basket, and a push under the boards which managed to upstage the entire cast.

So we were trailing 42 to 34 at the quarter break when Charley tapped my knee.

"Go in for Foot."

Charley's eyes were infested with an intensity I had never seen there before. It looked like he really wanted to win the ballgame. It was never too late . . . Ned Irish might be hovering about on green gossamer wings.

Or maybe Charley just wouldn't give up.

And when I indicated to Foot that I would be starting the second quarter, he nodded an exaggerated wink right in my face. Which gave me the impression that Foothead had somehow managed to curl the golden braid into a lasso, and that the Three Scabby Strumpets were now bound hand, tooth and tit . . . and the shredded script was stuffed into their mouths.

I felt the dislocation and tried to refocus my senses. The game had become a free square on the Bingo board,

a golden existential geo-globe which was independent of both the past and the future,
played in an arena governed by no known rules and no known odds.

The Elizabeth City Junior High School gymnasium had become the tangent point of two parallel galaxies.

Sandy brought the ball over the midcourt line where he was double-teamed . . . a tactic unheard of in an APBA ballgame. The increase in pressure and the gravitational panic forced Sandy to leave his feet and wildly throw the ball, and the onus, in the general direction of the basket. Hoping somebody would be there . . . but if they weren't, they should have been. And I was. But instead of taking a mildly complicated lay-up through Cody Wells, I flipped the ball to the corner where Will found himself in position for a naked fifteen-footer. Which he made. And raised his fist in my direction.

As we hustled back on defense, I shouted over to Sandy: "Nice pass."

One turnover later, I had the ball at the head of the foul circle . . . a couple of feet beyond my range. My flanks were unattended and before me stood Mister Box Canyon himself. His fists were fuming and he was waiting impatiently for me.

But someone pushed the catapult button and I shot the ball. It was a creaky, strained attempt to reach the basket . . . But the ball found its legs and crawled over the rim anyway.

The Miner fans had a collective grand mal, and I could see Charley holding one hand over his heart and madly waving instructions with the other. And sitting next to him on the bench, Pechman held his head and wailed of injustice and of lost receipts into the privacy of his hands.

The team started cooking. I stayed outside where TC couldn't get a clean shot at me . . . and where I even got an occasional pass. After we had tied the score, the Miner's coach started screaming at TC to play defense. But when he pawed the ground and charged at me in a straight line, it was an easy matter to run an Arctic Circle route around him to the basket for an easy lay-up.

The other end of the court, however, was strictly a nightmare. I couldn't hide on defense . . . and TC took full advantage of my dilemma. He went plain nuts. He pushed off . . . with the point of his elbow in the neck-shoulder valley where most of my cranial nerves had settled and were peacefully homesteading. He stomped on and pinned my right foot while he slugged my right hip . . . trying to disjoint me from ankle to asshole. He low-bridged me, high-bridged me and drawbridged me. While still bayoneting me with his elbows.

But I survived . . . I rolled and ducked and managed to stay on my feet. And everywhere I went, I held one exploring hand behind me and one forearm braced near my face.

And near the end of the half I even dared to get an offensive rebound. I pulled on TC's shorts from behind and he instinctively reached to pull them up. While he was back on his heels, I leaned over him and tipped the ball in.

And just before the buzzer, I added insult to humiliation. TC tried to force a hook pass to Brennan who was free underneath the basket . . . and it accidentally bounced off my wrist. Everybody else thought it was a blocked shot, so the building inhaled with terror and surprise as the half ended with the Rifles on top of an 82 to 76 score.

Some halftime dialogue:

"She said she wanted to give me some pussy, but her partner's husband was comin' home early so they both had to leave."

"That motherfucker never answered my question."

"I tol' her she could suck my dick if she lef' before I opened my eyes."

"You m'fuckaz bedda live me ilone fum now on."

"A fifteen-year-old bitch! So I told her I'd kick her ass if I caught her hanging around again. Shit . . . that's some hard nigger time on a chain gang if they catch you messing with that. And when I took off my clothes she started crying."

"That dickhead makes fifteen dollars a game more than me!"

"Where's some of that reefer at?"

Charley also let me start the second half. And TC looked subdued as we politely bopped fists in the center jump circle. But as a precaution, I conceded the tip to him—I actually jumped back at a 45-degree angle to keep his body away from mine.

But no matter.

Sandy stole the ball from Rubber, dribbled down court and we both noticed that Cody was now guarding me. He was quicker than TC and he had faster and more active hands, but I was four inches bigger and 40 pounds heavier.

Sandy cleared Will out of the corner so that I could work one-on-one . . . and he flipped me a perfectly placed rainbow pass.

I caught the ball, faked, turned and labored trying to get a good shot away. But I couldn't shake Cody. Then I fought my way to the top of my jump like a skindiver grasping for the surface.

And at the moment of release, a fuzzy shock wave relaxed my body, and flicked my wrist like a velvet slingshot arching feathers off a summer cliff.

Without following the trajectory of the ball, I turned up-court and raised my right fist as a libation.

As I passed Tarzan Cooper.

Whose eyes had an orgasm.

And he coiled his right arm and detonated the point of his elbow directly on the bridge of my nose.

WHAM!

I went numb from teeth to eyebrows as the first explosion indented my face. And then—speeded along by a pulsating fallout of pain—the mass of my nose approached infinity.

TC had blasted the middle of my face back into the vacuum from whence it had come.

And for a while, I had sincerely believed that I had beaten it ... That my calcium-deposited, ligament-strained, tendon-stretched ankles had sprouted wings.

When the gong stopped vibrating, the pain was so intense that it short-circuited and overloaded every synapse in the area. It was like the colored lights traveling around a marquee ... but with a few bulbs mercifully extinguished.

And after the universe had stopped fibrillating, a troupe of baggy-pants vaudevillians came time-stepping out onto the center of the stage.

It's a good thing my nose didn't hurt when I laughed.

CHAPTER Fifteen

RIFLES				MINERS			
	FG	FT	P		FG	FT	P
Jones	4	1-3	9	Simonds	23	9-10	55
Freeman	16	5-5	37	Brennan	9	14-17	32
McLean	3	2-3	8	Cooper	5	3-5	13
King	5	0-1	10	Wells	10	1-1	21
Williams	20	1-1	41	Middleton	5	3-4	13
Fitzgerald	2	0-0	4	Johnson	3	1-1	7
Lassner	9	0-0	18	Hamilton	2	0-0	4
Paterson	3	2-2	8	Daniels	0	4-5	4
Wilson	1	0-0	2				
Mathews	4	1-1	9				

RIFLES	34	48	22	34 —	138
MINERS	42	34	37	36 —	149

OVERTIME

CHAPTER SIXTEEN

PECHMAN'S NEPHEW DROVE ME TO THE HOSPITAL. His name was Sherman, and rumor has it that he was booted out of some local junior college because of low grades. So Pechman had taken him in as an indentured flunky. But the family line was, "Sherman is learning the business from Uncle Arnold."

Sherman wears long-sleeved paisley shirts buttoned to the throat—and his idol is Bowie Kuhn. But in spite of this, Sherman does have his functions: he doles out the "free" passes to the ballplayers, and he chauffeurs injured superstars to the nearest free emergency clinic.

Sherman is also an avid student of the human condition.

"You played a nice game," he said as he stopped for a red light.

"Nyes," I answered.

Then, five minutes later: "Say, Bo . . . is it true that you guys get to sleep with a lot of women?"

"Nyes."

But his eagerly inclined head was insistent.

"We get laid a lot in the hotel . . ."

"Yeah?"

" . . . but most of the guys get most of their pussy . . . "

"Yeah? Yeah?"

" . . . in the john in the locker room."

"Yeah???"

"Sure. Why do you think Unca Arnold knocks before he comes in?"

"I don't know."

"That's right."

But the throbbing was increasing in volume and resonance. "Listen, Sherman. We sneak all the chicks into the locker room about three hours before game time. So why don't you get there earlier and hide out in the equipment locker? You can see everything and then leave after the game starts."

"Yeah! Yeah!"

Sherman dropped me off at the Our Lady of the True Believer Hospital on the outskirts of Elizabeth City (i.e., near the coal mines), and he gave me five bucks for a cab ride back to the hotel.

"Don't tell Uncle Arnold about this. I'll say to him that I stayed here with you. Otherwise I'll have to go back to the game . . . or he'll deduct it from your salary. Okay?"

"You're a wise man, Sherman."

As I walked through the parking lot to the clinic I realized I was still wearing my basketball uniform, and that it was starting to snow.

The two buildings looked like a brace of dusty, unkept mausoleums . . . and there was a blank gray slab directly over the entrance to the larger one. Begging for an iron flame to descend and carve out a suitable inscription. And a laser beam emanated from the center of the slightly dented equator on my face . . . and it flicked out something else I had been forced to memorize as part of my education:

"I am the way into the city of woe.
I am the way to a forsaken people.
I am the way into eternal sorrow.

Sacred justice moved my architect.
I was raised here by divine omnipotence,
Primordial love and ultimate intellect.

Only those elements time cannot wear
Were made before me, and beyond time I stand.
Abandon all hope ye who enter here."

That's just what happens when you let sinners into the neighborhood—everybody's real estate depreciates.

But no inscription could do justice to the inside of the clinic. There were actually a few strands of straw on the floor of the waiting room and I had the distinct feeling that I was about to be shackled to a wall and fed gruel and water until I either healed or died.

The nurse at the desk didn't bat an eye when she saw me.

"Lassner in for Foothead Jones," I told her.

But she just smiled and handed me a piece of paper. "Please take a seat and wait until your number is called."

"Hey, listen . . . before I waste a lot of time . . . Do you have a nice prune danish? Or a pumpernickel with seeds that's not burnt on the bottom? If not, I'll go somewhere else . . . "

Still smiling, she pushed a button on a switchboard console to her left and said once more: "Please take a seat and wait until your number is called."

I sat down next to a knife-thin man I thought was in black-

177

face until he coughed and some of his makeup shook off in a fine ebony powder. He was sucking on a tank of oxygen.

Next to him was a sturdy teenage lad who was holding a towel to his face. I could see the blood frozen in dark stripes along his arms and down the front of his shirt.

In the row behind us, a fiercely regal-looking old woman dressed in a frayed house dress sat with one spidery arm in a dirty sling. Which had been torn from an old lace petticoat.

And a slope-faced mountain woman sat hunched as she daintily nursed a gasping yellow infant.

The straw was supposed to soak up the blood and the other seepings.

My number was 27—the Holy Trinity cubed. Almost as good as a clove of garlic.

A few minutes later, the other end of the pushed button came over to investigate. It was a tall black man, with a surprisingly elongated cranium, and he was outfitted to look like an intern. I wished I had a big cigar and a moustache.

"Hello," he said.

"Hello yourself."

"You causing any trouble?"

I pointed to my uniform. "Wait a minute. Aren't you a member of the Inner City Blues? You mean the game isn't tonight . . .?"

He performed a very acceptable imitation of human laughter. "Everything's going to be fine," he said.

Then he reached into a secluded pocket and pulled out a small green capsule. Which he slipped into my hand in a very, very surreptitious manner.

"You may need this," he said out of the corner of his mouth.

"You'll probably be here for a while. Saturday night's a big night here."

And then he winked and left the room.

Things seemed to be under control. The pill had moved the pain and numbness by at least three perimeters, so I was free to watch the show.

First there was the bedpan brigade. As a pretty candy stripette sauntered carefully by, I let out a muted screech and went to pinch her ass. But she didn't spill a drop.

The next celebrant appeared to be Xyggletrop cleverly disguised as a Chinese brain surgeon. He was talking to what appeared to be another doctor.

"Would you believe he wanted to be a writer? The shock treatment didn't work so we had to perform a lobotomy. You remember him . . . the one who insisted his name was Joyce Finnegan. Maybe we should have cut off his balls also."

They both laughed.

Then Xyggletrop smiled slyly at his companion. "Say, you couldn't lend me a gleeb until pay day, could you?"

After they left, a security guard walked by listening to a walkie-talkie. He stopped to light a cigarette and placed his communicator on an empty seat next to me. Where I could hear the broadcast:

"Hello? This is Duffy's Tavern. Where the élite meet to eat. Duffy ain't here, this is Archie the manager speaking."

"Duh . . . duh, hello, Arch."

"Oh, hello, Finnegan. I thought you was Mrs. Duffy looking for Duffy."

Then the cop picked up the machine, looked at me, and said, "X27 . . . X27 . . . Pick up . . . Roger, Wilco. A ham and swiss on white bread with mayonnaise. Over and out."

My next visitor was a totally bald, middle-aged squint of a man, wearing a blood-splattered smock, a pince-nez, a pair of oily leather boots and smoking a cigarette from a long red holder. He bowed stiffly and handed me a card:

DOKTOR WOLFGANG VON KRONKITE
—BONES SET
—WARTS REMOVED
—ALGEBRA TUTORING
SPECIALTY—HEEL TATTOOES OBLITERATED

"At your service," he said as he slapped a swagger stick against his thigh. And he turned to address the small knot of students who had been standing at attention one respectful pace behind him.

"Now shtudents . . . you will notice zat zis young Semite's schnozz has been geshmashed. Now vat would be za proper medicinal treatment? You . . . Fritz . . .?"

Fritz saluted smartly and barked out his answer: "Herr Doktor Kronkite, sir! The correct medical procedure would be to take X-rays of the patient's nasal area. Sir!"

"Nein! Nein! Dumkopf!" Kronkite snarled as he struck Fritz about the face with his swagger stick. "Za beezer ist already broken, fool! You vould risk sterilizibination for a bent hook? Svine! You . . . Hans!"

Hans goose-stepped forward.

"The proper procedure, Herr Doktor, is to take the subject's temperature, give him two aspirins and an extra ration of sausage . . . and send him back to the front."

"Nein! Nein! Shvinehundt! Imbecile! Mussa-fokker! Did you not hear me say zat zis Jewish pig vas a Semite?"

Kronkite's chest swelled as the still-trembling students began writing.

"Za correct procedure is to remove za patient's gold fillings!"

As the students buzzed with admiration, Kronite turned to me again.

"You have, perhaps, relatives in Ber . . ."

Fritz cleared his throat loudly.

". . . er . . . in Elizabeth City? In Elizabeth City!"

"No," I said. "But I do have influential friends in Buenos Aires."

Kronkite clicked his heels and bowed his head precisely. Then he started poking and probing at my nose. While the students recorded every "Aha!" and "Tsk!" Tsk!"

Then Kronkite withdrew two long metal rods from a shoulder holster and delicately inserted one into each nostril. And without a word of warning, he quickly manuevered the rods in a tight semicircle . . . snapping the bone back into its proper position. Then, as he was withdrawing his instruments, Kronkite twisted the rods a little to the left . . . giving my hithertofore button-nose a humped, dog-leg left.

I looked at Hans and smiled. "You will notice," I said, "that Dr. Kronkite has taken special pains to make sure you won't make the same error again. You will also notice that the Third Reich turned out much better than anyone could have imagined."

Kronite nodded in approval and waved the students out of the room.

"Herr Lassner, you vill bleed on za shtraw, please. It makes better bricks for za commonvolk, forshtehen sie? Und you vill go to shleep ven you get home, ozzerzevize you vill look for several days very tallow . . . But everyting vill be hokay. You shouldn't vorry, boychick. Eat a bissel chicken zoop und a piece rye bread, mit a half sour pickle und a piece fruit und a glass borscht. Und call your Mama every day no matter vat on za telephone. Bubbala . . . all you got is one Mama."

Then he shuffled off into the parking lot alternately mumbling "Adonoi," chanting the Lord's Prayer in Latin and crossing himself from left to right.

NETWORK
TIME OUT

CHAPTER Seventeen

I HAD A STRANGE DREAM when I finally fell asleep back at the hotel. I dreamed that I had filled an eyedropper with the water of life.,

and snorted three drops up into my sinuses,
and it was vapid, tasteless, colorless,
and a universal solvent to boot.
And it *will* be fire next time . . .
A candle, not a tree,
a meaningless instant when a sluice of flame
leaps from the wick . . .
and lives by its own brilliance
and smiths its own form,
but which passes so rapidly that a passerby can only
discern a suggestion of its existence.
A candle-fire which will roast the suet off the brain
and then crisp it all to nothing.

Then a chorus line of cunty Seven-Up bottles danced out, singing of hot dogs, peanuts and ice cream. And Mr. Popcorn made a rare personal appearance to announce that there would be a slight intermission and that the refreshment stand was open.

And I did have to take a piss. But the floor was cold and the bed was warm . . . so I dreamed a coming-attractions trailer of

"Bo Pees in the Sink." I had to run it three times before my bladder was convinced it had already been emptied.

The next flick was a dramatization of some kind of computer basketball game ... As a posed shot of each starting player appeared on the screen, a copper-and-wire voice provided the vital statistics. Then each player made a pregame assessment and prediction.

THE STARTING LINE-UP FOR ... AWK ... WHIRR ... UNCLE JOHN'S BAND ... AT ONE FORWARD, 6-2, 210 POUNDS, SHOOTS LEFT ... JIMI HENDRIX.

"Ha, ha ... .it's me again. Isn't that a gas? And I'd just like to say that there are, you know, enough rational-negative factors ... like Stonehenge, man, and Easter Island, and Groucho Marx, and Judge Crater, man ... and Jimi too ... so that positron logic can't work at all, man. So like we got to ... we just got to ... play a zone defense just to stay in the ballgame. See y'all after the game."

"AT THE OTHER FORWARD, 6-7, 210 POUNDS, SHOOTS LEFT ... JULIUS OF ERVING."

"I'm hip that the worst thing a person can do with responsibility is to ignore it. I mean, I didn't go looking for it ... it just came to me because of what I am. If I don't help people, I'm hurting them. What I have learned is to be tactful with those people who try to take liberties with me, who want the use of my name and my money. Some ballplayers like to surround themselves with back-slappers, free-loaders and whatnot, but the good thoughts of my family and friends are enough for me. But the most callous I can be is to let the phone ring when it all gets too heavy. And it does cause some changes ... I'm more of a commodity than a person to some people,

186

and that affects the way they act toward me and the way I react to them.

"Anyway . . . we're going to be whipping some ass tonight!"

"AT CENTER, 6-9, 220 POUNDS . . . BILL RUSSELL."

"All I can say is that I'm very happy to be here as a representative of Mommy Bell. And I'm also very happy that nobody ever made a big stink about the rubber plantations and the nigger slaves that I own in Libya. And we can't lose the game, you see, because I never miss a shot on camera."

"AT ONE GUARD, 5-6, 142 POUNDS, SHOOTS LEFT . . . THE ORIGINAL DR. J. . . . JUDAS ISCARIOT."

"Listen . . . it's a good life, let me tell you. You wouldn't believe the money I make just for endorsements. And let me tell you something . . . for a few pieces of silver, you can even buy a referee. What do you think of that?"

"AND AT THE OTHER GUARD, 5-9, 175 POUNDS, SHOOTS LEFT . . . TY COBB."

"I ain't got nothin' to say to you fucken frontrunnin' fuck-faces . . . Let's get the fucken game started . . ."

AND NOW INTRODUCING THE HOME TEAM . . . THE HOLLYWOOD SQUARES. AT ONE FORWARD, 6-2, 190 POUNDS, SHOOTS RIGHT . . . BRIGHAM YOUNG."

"Hello, brethren. You will notice that there are no niggers on our squad . . . and no women either. Righteousness cannot be compromised. Whenever you are tempted and torn with doubt, remember the statue of yours truly that the faithful have erected in front of the Mormon Tabernacle in Salt Lake City. It has its ass facing the temple and an outstretched palm

187

turned toward the Zion National Bank. And remember that the smart money is always on us."

"AT THE OTHER FORWARD, 6-4, 225 . . . ERNEST HEMINGWAY."

"Bonus notches, amiggers! Before I blew my head off with a shotgun, I wrote something in lipstick on the mirror in my bathroom: 'I can't help it! Please stop me from writing!' So if we can control them off the boards, and if we can keep our hands off their cute little bodies and avoid foul trouble, we should win."

"AT CENTER, 8-11½, 903 POUNDS, SHOOTS BOTH RIGHT AND LEFT . . . AWK . . . RASP . . . GACK . . . JESUS OF NAZARETH."

"A certain man had a fig tree planted in his vineyard; and he came and sought fruit thereon, and found none.

"Then he said unto the dresser of his vineyard, Behold, these three years I come seeking fruit on this fig tree, and find none: cut it down; why cumbereth it the ground?

"And he answering said unto him, Lord, let it alone this year also, till I shall dig about it, and dung it:

"And if it bear fruit, well: and if not, then after that thou shalt cut it down. . . .

"And when he saw a fig tree in the way, he came to it, and found nothing thereon, but leaves only, and said unto it, Let no fruit grow on thee henceforward forever. And presently the fig tree withered away.

"This parable meaneth that the ballgame shall be determined by how closely the officials shall call goaltending and who keeps score. Amen."

"AT ONE GUARD, 5-8, 172 POUNDS ... RICHARD MILHOUS NIXON."

"It was owned by a little old Unitarian lady ... really ... and all she ever used it for was to drive to church. It has a new tranny, new rubber and new brakes. Believe me, it's a cream puff. If I'm lyin', I'm dyin'."

"AND AT THE OTHER GUARD, 5-4, 87 POUNDS ... AUGUSTINE OF HIPPO."

"Listen to me, you sinful pieces of shit. If it feels good and you do it, I'll get my stepfather to kick the piss out of you."

Well, that was enough for my poor cowardly kidneys. And I figured that the arbitrary accumulation of urine was definitely as legitimate a sign from the gods as a prophetic dream anyway. So I got out of bed and relieved myself into the sink.

And I loved the smell of my own wasted cells,
the stink of my own shit
my privately pungent farts
and the acidic breath of my underarms.
I even love the taste of heartburn.
I always eat my dead nails,
my crusty scabs
and my surplus snot.

It was only twenty minutes past midnight, early enough to call Rachael at the bookstore. She answered after the first ring: "Hello. Village Books."

"Hi, Rachael. This is Bo."

"Oh, hi! You sound kind of funny. I didn't recognize your voice."

"I know . . . I have a bad cold. How have you been?"

"Okay . . . I just sort of expected to see you around here the last couple of days. We just received a shipment of foundling books that you might be interested in."

"Sounds good. I know calling you like this is a bummer, but it's the only thing I could work out."

"That's cool," she said. "I can dig it."

"Hey . . . why don't we get together then . . . you know . . . see each other . . ."

"You mean like a date, right?"

"Something like that."

"Fine," she said. "Great. I get off at one tomorrow night."

"Okay. I'll see you then."

"So long."

"Bye."

But I had missed the ballgame. A science-fiction movie was now showing. I had already missed the beginning, so I really couldn't figure out the plot. But:

There was a little Jap making a fortune selling monster insurance in Tokyo.

There was an American jock-scientist (played by Nick Adams), who kept talking about the expanding and contracting universe.

There was a German scientist saying that with each succeeding cycle of cosmic regeneration, all of us will *déjà-vu* more and more of the future. And each generation will have a tougher and tougher battle defending its own time period from an invasion by the past.

But everybody in the movie lived happily ever after . . .

They all wound up in shrines watching flicks of their own lives . . .

Which they lived in the wake of their own futures.

But I gave it only a candle and a half . . . you couldn't Danse to it and I didn't like the ending.

CHAPTER Eighteen

I slept until 1:30 Sunday afternoon, ate some eggs in the diner down the street, paid 75 cents a pound for *The New York Times* and returned to the hotel to while away the rest of the day.

I could have sent for a bellhop, paid him two bucks and had him bring a television set up to the room. But Sunday afternoons are invariably littered with wretched refuse like golf tournaments, bowling, tennis, car races, hockey and football —and I hate them all.

Golf is a ride through the park taken by fat businessmen, bull dykes and drawling plastic humanoids . . . who think that wearing plaid pants and Banlon shirts qualifies them as athletes.

And all of the excitement was taken out of bowling when they invented the automatic pin spotter. This eliminated the drama of a nimble black urchin in a specially designed pit trying to avoid being brained by flying pins and errant bowling balls. When I was a kid, I actually believed that wiping out the pin boy was the object of the game . . . But any sport where a one-armed sixty-year-old man in a wheelchair can beat a spry, jockstrap-wearing teenager should be taken about as seriously as a red-hot monopoly game.

But tennis is the most detestable of all. Aristocratic suburban housefraus and ambitious executives take lessons from "marvelous" teaching pros inside plastic bubbles, and then arrogantly jog through the streets wearing red velour warm-up suits with white stripes running down the arms and legs. Substitute a stick with a nail on one end for their tennis rackets, and they'd all look like Department of Parks shit pickers.

Car racing is watched with interest only by those among us who want to commit suicide but don't have the balls to do it.

Hockey is another boring spectacle. All anybody ever does is give and go, and almost all goals are accidents. If there were no such thing as professional hockey, everybody in the NHL and WHA would either be in the roller derby, or wearing masks or overalls and wrestling in small Yukon towns.

And any sport that canonizes a prick like Vince Lombardi should not be seen by children. But every Sunday afternoon, Joe Boff has the little woman make four ham-and-cheese heroes, fetch a cold six-pack of Budweiser, and set it all on a bridge table in front of the TV. Then, when the kids are safely ensconced at a neighbor's, Joe puts a jockstrap over his nose, and watches six consecutive hours of professional football.

And he thinks you have to be a genius to understand the game. He has memorized all the jargon—the Z-out, the sack, the stunt, the 43 red stack left motion right on 2 hut hut . . .

But he doesn't know what Bob Griese really tells Paul Warfield in the huddle: "Go out to the green Chevy and cut right." Or what instructions are actually imparted to Larry Little: "Whoever's in front of you, knock him on his fucken ass."

The only other fare on the Sabbath television menu is strictly dessert: old Tarzan movies, cultural programs which feature a half-hour closeup of a Ming vase, and political parfait like "Issues and Evasions." So I was more than content to read my way through the *Times* and listen to the radio. There was an all-news station, a country-western station and a Jesus station. Which, of course, I listened to.

"Friends . . . we will get back to our sermon after I tell all you wonderful Christian people about a brand new inspirational cereal called Cross Puffs. Each box of Cross Puffs contains thousands of tiny wheat kernels which have been baked and puffed into the shape of the One, the Only . . . yes, friends in Christ, the True Cross. So that when we eat our breakfast with our loved ones, we can remember our poor, bleeding Savior who suffered so that products like Cross Puffs could be available to all of us. Cross Puffs are made of the same flour as the holy wafer, friends. From a secret Oral Roberts recipe.

"My blessed friends . . . wouldn't you like to have Jesus Christ flowing in your veins, giving you the spirit, the strength and the vitamins needed to combat the devil's sinful legions? And they are numerous, my friends, so be sure to order the Titanic size.

"And Cross Puffs come in Omni-Frutti flavor for the kiddies. They're sweet enough so that your little darling children will not be tempted to accept candy from any Commie-rapist-atheist-rapist-Jew-rapist-nigro-rapist strangers. Your child can have Jesus Himself flowing in his Sweet Tooth.

"So friends, send only five dollars for a ten-year supply. That's right . . . only five dollars for a ten-year supply of Cross Puffs. Payment thereof shall indicate acceptance of a lifetime membership in the Smile, Jesus Loves You Social Club and Real Estate Development Co. And payer will thereby agree to pay all dues which will be determined at a later date."

A couple of hours later I went out for some Chinese food which I ate in the room. On my way back up in the elevator, I was joined by a bunch of people wearing convention badges:

"Hello my name is _____. Pittsburgh Paints Can Color the World." And they were all in costume ... and all very drunk. A pair of dice, a pirate, a ghost and a gladiatress got off at the second floor. Leaving me alone in the elevator with a turtle.

The smell of the Chinese food I was carrying made me fart very loudly. So I quickly darted an indignant look at the turtle.

"Jesus Christ!" I said. "Some people just don't have no fucken manners."

CHAPTER Nineteen

As I walked over to the gym, I passed dusty acres of squashed houses. Which were collectively buckling and fulminating in several different directions at the same time. And every block had its old witches rocking on faded porches and staring out at me. Old women with dust-filled wrinkles, knitting their own funeral shawls.

I said "Hello, Grannie" to each of them, but no one answered . . . and no one dropped a pearl.

Wellington Junior High is built in a cavity between two slight hills. And it looked as ancient, as beaten and as senseless as a red brick shithouse in the middle of Death Valley. The walls were lacking any ornamental gargoyles, or griffins, or lions reading books. The only indication a wayward tourist would have that the building wasn't a factory or a museum was a single wooden sign stuck into the front lawn.

The people pushing in to see the game were dressed in their usual mackinaws and red-and-black checkered jackets. Like extras in a Lum 'n Abner movie.

The younger revelers were bobby-soxers and greasers from nearby Boondock Tech. They felt that the game was just an excuse to holler and curse and exercise their technique in public.

And every member of the visiting team looked either like Boss Tweed, Abbie Hoffman, Attila the Hun or Eldridge Cleaver.

Pechman was already inside the team locker room ...
impatiently waiting to speak to me. And everybody was pissed
at me for giving Pechman reason enough for being there. I
mean ... a ballplayer does need some private time to stretch
his lungs and fire his head before an important ballgame.

As soon as I came through the door, Pechman jumped on me
... and he stuck like dog shit on a pair of rippled sole shoes.

"How are you? How's your nose feel? Don't worry about
the cab fare and the emergency-room charge ... It's all on the
house. Do you think you can play? I sent Sherman all the way
over to Reading to get you a goalie's mask, so you can wear it
over your nose."

He paused to sidle lewdly up next to me. "I'll make it worth
your while," he whispered hoarsely.

"That's very good," I said. "What other impressions do you
do?"

"Ha! Ha! Here ... try it on and see if it fits."

But Sherman was timidly mincing into the locker room.

"Hey, Uncle Arnold," he said too loudly. "I put in those
extra seats on the stage like you said. Do you want me to
reopen the box office now?"

Uncle Arnold snapped his nephew a "Don't bother me, you
fool" swipe of his hand.

"Looks like the swelling's gone down," Pechman said.

"Some."

"But you still look a little ... spaced out," he said with a
proud grin.

And then I sang him a line from "Voodoo Chile": "I'm a
million miles away ... and right here in your picture frame."

I grabbed the mask, crossed my eyes and smiled him on out
of the room.

Before Sandy and Foot got a chance to reoccupy the toilet
stall, I jumped onto the seat to take my pregame shit. Al-

though I rarely think of my own shit as shit. It's more like a cathartic exodus of twice-dead things from the bondage of my still-living body.

And as I sat there, engulfed by the sounds and smells, I hoped that I would die the way I shat. Loosely, quickly and with satisfaction.

And I decided to leave my bowels to science.

Right after we took alyups, I had to walk over to the bench and sit down. My nose was throbbing and bumping up against the inside of the mask.

Charlie came over and sat down beside me. "How do you feel, kid?"

"Not too bad, coach."

He twitched his head in surprise. "It's funny . . . but I guess nobody's called me coach in a long time."

I grunted ambiguously.

"If you don't think you can make it, then sit it out. The bastard is gonna get his blood money either way."

"What the fuck, Charlie. I signed my name to the fucken contract same as him. Really, it doesn't hurt too bad. Why don't I run up and down the floor a couple of minutes into the second quarter . . . ? Then everybody'll be happy. I could play a one-man zone, away from TC . . . cut off passes and stuff. He'll take the jump shot anyway . . . "

But Charlie was gone into the past: "That Clair Bee . . . that drunken old bastard. Ever hear of him, kid?"

"No."

"He knew more fucken zones . . . Playing a team of his was like playing a team of fucken spiders. Wherever you turned, there was a hand in your face . . . and it made you all crazy and impatient . . . like you wanted to be somewheres else. That old bastard . . . He's dead I heard."

He looked to me for confirmation.

"I didn't even know he was sick," I said.

And I was the recipient of my second weird-look exit of the evening.

The game itself progressed just about the same as all the Rifles' previous home games had. The only unexpected development being that Rubber Simonds was having an exceptional night. His shots were wristed high and with perfect rotation. And more often than any natural law could explain, they hit the hole in the bottom of the net . . . causing the limp strings to jounce back up through the rim. Regardless of the angle or the distance, the net did its sprightly dance again and again.

Rubber was, in fact, so dangerous, that he had already been whistled to the bench with four fouls when Charlie sent me in midway through the second quarter.

As Foothead passed me on the way to the bench, he tapped lightly on my mask: "Too bad you ain't got another nose to turn to thine enemies, rookie."

TC seemed perhaps a little fiercer than usual, but I really hadn't been following his antics too closely. Rubber's cord-poppers were far more intriguing. But I was careful nevertheless, and I skirted TC's boundaries as though he were a walking shower of leprosy.

And whenever I found myself with the ball, I made no pretense of even attempting a shot. Needless to say, I also stayed far removed from the boards. But apparently my movements were still too offensive to suit TC, because he took advantage of our unavoidable proximity during a foul shot to hit me with a moderate rib bender.

Charlie saw it too, and he immediately took me out of the game. To a very healthy square of applause.

I was resting maskless on the bench for about two minutes, when Foothead called a time-out and came hobbling over to the sideline.

"I do believe I twisted my ankle," he drawled. And he clucked his tongue at me: "Ain' that unfortunate?"

Charlie sent Sherman back down to the locker room for a roll of adhesive tape. And he sent me right back into the ballgame.

Will was shooting two free throws, and as I lined up next to TC, I tried communicating with him.

"Hey, big man . . . Enough. Okay?" And I pointed to my mask.

He turned his face toward me, but I couldn't tell exactly where he was looking.

"I ain' gonna lose," he said with great intensity. "I ain' gonna lose no more."

Will made his first shot and I glanced for the first time at the scoreboard. We were ahead by 17.

"But, TC," I said, "you can't win here. You're in Wellington, Pennsylvania, in the APBA, man . . . Not Hollywood, not Heaven, and definitely not Harlem."

His eyes seemed to be oozing slightly. "I ain' goin' out a loser."

Will missed the second shot, and TC attacked the rebound with one hand and my face with the other. While I was thinking that I had just wasted three good metaphors, he pounded a hard shot to my forehead. Just above the mask.

I was more stunned than hurt, and the first thing I found myself doing was looking at the closest official with complete outrage.

"Play ball," he said. "No harm, no foul."

And I realized that TC had been right all along. That he was the only one who saw through the skeleton of the rules and the subrules

and their corrupt enforcers . . .

the huge molasses of people screaming and cheering for other people they think they know

and are positive they own.

He saw the players fighting like rats in a barrel

for more playing time

on clocks that go from zero to twenty-four

and back to sunrise again.

Until the buzzer deafens the players and ends the game. But there's always the possibility of infinite overtimes, where the G's and the air are Saturnian, but where each point scored counts double.

And where a good shooter can make a good living.

Sandy gave me the ball at least twenty feet out, but he cut to the basket before I could return it to him. As I pivoted to find him, I saw TC puffing steam from his ears, flames from his ass and headed straight at me like I was Pauline Peril tied to the track and about to be ravaged by the 9:14 out of Topeka.

But I managed to time it just right. As he got closer, I faced him head to head and heaved up a wild one-hander . . . throwing my right knee upward and forward.

And I blasted that motherfucker right between his cannon balls.

He fell screaming to the ground, holding both hands to his crotch. For an instant the crowd was terror-stricken, and TC's pain-garbled hysteria crackled and rebounded throughout the entire building.

Then the official blew his whistle and dramatically indicated that not only had the ball gone in, but that TC was also charged with a foul.

A three-point play the hard way.

As the security police dragged TC out the front door like a dying, shivering bull, I calmly sank the foul shot.

And the net did its dance for me.

"IN A BASKETBALL GAME PLAYED IN UNIVAC STADIUM, THE HOLLYWOOD SQUARES DEFEATED UNCLE JOHN'S BAND ... THE SQUARES CENTER, HELD SCORELESS ALL THROUGH REGULATION TIME, ERUPTED ... IN ... THE ... RUPTURED ... SQUWAK ... GASP ..."

UNCLE JOHN'S BAND

	min	fgm	fga	ftm	fta	r	a	s	f	tp
Hendrix	53	8	17	8	10	16	7	3	3	24
Erving	53	10	21	7	9	15	6	2	4	27
Russell	53	5	11	2	4	24	4	1	3	3
Iscariot	52	3	5	2	2	0	5	14	6	8
Cobb	53	11	21	9	9	7	5	5	5	31
Lassner	1	1	1	1	1	0	0	0	0	3

HOLLYWOOD SQUARES

	min	fgm	fga	ftm	fta	r	a	s	f	tp
Young	53	12	27	4	5	14	0	0	4	28
Hemingway	53	0	0	0	0	0	0	0	5	0
Christ	53	31	31	10	10	48	23	19	0	72
St. Aug.	53	16	18	15	15	5	15	12	3	47
Nixon	53	7	68	0	0	0	0	7	5	14

	1	2	3	4	ovt
Bums	26	26	26	26	0 — 104
Bd. of D.	26	26	26	26	72 — 176

CHAPTER TWENTY

WE DIDN'T LEAVE WELLINGTON until well after midnight. Lacey and Will were galavanting around town, doing some instant celebrating. While Foot and I waited, perched on a couch in a dark corner of the Jermyn Hotel's front lobby. Where we smoked our heads off, and giggled uncontrollably every time we looked at each other.

So all four of us were wasted and rowdy as we headed for New York. And about halfway there, as we hummed along the Pennsylvania Thruway, Lacey peeped into the rearview mirror and announced a guest.

"The man," he said.

I thought the siren and the flashing red light were kind of cute myself, but everybody else seemed to be petrified. As Lacey pulled up and stopped on the shoulder of the road, he flicked his head back at me and ordered me "Be cool."

The trooper strode menacingly up to the side of the car. His eyes were crouched like steel springs under his wide-brimmed Boy Scout hat. And I decided to say something to let him know that I wasn't being kidnapped.

"Hello, ociffer."

But all he did was unbutton his holster flap.

"License and registration, boy."

And as he fumbled with his wallet, I could hear Lacey mumbling and moaning low: "This white boy gonna get us *all* in trouble."

"What seems to be the problem?" I asked the cop.

He shined his flashlight on my innocent, smiling face. "Just a routine check."

This was the moment I had been waiting for. "Foothead!" I exclaimed. "The man wants to check our routine!"

Foot unfolded one of his especially sly grins. "Who was that ugly ol' white bitch I saw you fuckin' last night?"

"That was no ugly ol' white bitch . . . That was your mother."

And in perfect unison, we turned left to face the trooper . . . and presented him with our outstretched left palms.

He returned a silly grin as he handed me Lacey's credentials. "I ain't never heard that one before," he said.

And then he let us go.

I had to wait until Monday night to catch up with Rachael. But she was still there on her perch beside the cash register when I walked into the store. And she did a strange double-take when she saw me.

"How you doing?" I said. "Sorry I couldn't make it last night. We didn't get home from the game until after this place was closed. I hope you didn't wait for me too long. Let's go get some eats and I'll tell you why I love you so much."

And those wonderful cloud-gray eyes didn't even flicker as she turned to me and said: "Are you fucking kidding? I hate to say it, but you blew it last night. I stayed open for a half hour waiting on you. And just before I closed, Rock Lock came in and he browsed through some transcendental meditation books up there on the top row. So go take your show some-place else."

flap . . . flap . . . flap . . .flap . . . flap . . . flap . . . flap . . .